Bible Crossword Puzzles

TEST YOUR BIBLE KNOWLEDGE

Publications International, Ltd.

Harvey Estes is an ordained United Methodist minister. He served in a parish for seven years before becoming a full-time crossword puzzle constructor. His puzzles have been published in several publications including *The New York Times, The Wall Street Journal, The Washington Post,* and Simon & Schuster. He also authored *Coat of Many Crosswords,* a book of Bible-themed puzzles for adults.

Kelly Clark creates weekly crossword puzzles for her church based on the Sunday's Mass Readings and Psalm Response. She is also a puzzle contributor to *The New York Times, The Wall Street Journal, Games Magazine,* and Simon & Schuster crossword puzzle books. She received the Margaret Award for best puzzle in Simon & Schuster's *Series 233 Crossword Puzzle Book.*

Diane Epperson is a professional crossword puzzle constructor who has been published in *The New York Times, The Washington Post, The Los Angeles Times, The New York Sun,* and many other publications. In addition to her secular puzzles, she has had several Bible-themed puzzles published online by Universal Crosswords.

Terry Hall is an ordained minister who has served ten years on the Bible faculty at the Moody Bible Institute in Chicago. He is also a professional crossword puzzle constructor who has authored several books including *The Complete Book of Bible Trivia Crosswords* and *78 Great Fun and Challenging Bible Crosswords.*

Louis Weber, CEO
Publications International, Ltd.
7373 North Cicero Avenue
Lincolnwood, Illinois 60712

ISBN-13: 978-1-4127-0045-0
ISBN-10: 1-4127-0045-0

Manufactured in USA

8 7 6 5 4 3 2 1

Puzzles Just for You

Do you enjoy solving crossword puzzles that really challenge your Bible knowledge and are fun at the same time? The clever crosswords in this book are thoroughly entertaining *and* challenge your knowledge of the Bible.

You'll need to know the books of the Bible, key characters and events in the Old and New Testaments, and important Bible verses. (We've used the King James Version unless otherwise noted.) The puzzles at the beginning of the book are the easiest, and they increase in difficulty through to the back of the book. Your crossword skills will also be tested in many other subject areas, from science to history to entertainment. Of course, popular culture, whether in Bible times or today, will pop up frequently.

These crosswords are designed for puzzlers who want their puzzles based on Bible themes and who enjoy racking their brains. Once you get started, you won't be able to quit.

Affirming God Forever

Across

1. Prophetess mentioned in Luke 2:36
5. Laban's elder daughter (Genesis 29:16)
9. Place for calves (Malachi 4:2)
14. Timely blessing
15. Pelvic bones
16. Divided Asian nation
17. Enthusiastic
18. With 60-Across, the start of our affirmation (Matthew 6:13)
20. David's home, in 1 Chronicles 11:7
22. Gulf War missile
23. Snoops might peer through one
25. Possessed influence, so to speak
30. Napolean, in Elba
32. Singer Francis
33. Support
36. *Citizen* ___
38. Smells
39. Aviation prefix
40. Schoolboy collars
42. Jesus saw Nathanael under one (John 1:48)
43. Paul anticipated one "of righteousness" (2 Timothy 4:8)
45. Prefix meaning "outside"
46. Dame Myra the pianist
47. Get, as a radio broadcast
49. "Get thee ___, Satan" (Matthew 4:10)
51. Breathed noisily, like a horse
53. Camp out, instead of staying at hotel
57. "For ye have the ___ always with you" (Matthew 26:11)
59. Cat
60. See 18-Across (Matthew 6:13)
65. Algerian seaport
66. Archaeological find
67. Spy ___ Hari
68. Attorney general under Clinton
69. How a confident solver might solve
70. "For Sarah conceived, and bare Abraham ___" (Genesis 21:2)
71. Strategic World War I Belgian river

Down

1. Taken ___ (surprised)
2. Starbursts
3. Clamorous
4. With 26-Down, our affirmation continues (Matthew 6:13)
5. Realistic
6. "Evil Woman" band, for short
7. Broadcasts
8. "They ___ cockatrice' eggs . . ." (Isaiah 59:5)
9. Vamoose
10. Heavy weight
11. "The words of the Lord ___ pure words" (Psalm 12:6)
12. Honolulu garland
13. ___ Cruces, New Mexico
19. 1950s antisubversive grp.
21. Bagel go-with
24. Overjoy
26. See 4-Down (Matthew 6:13)
27. Siesta sound
28. Buenos ___, Argentina
29. Affirmative replies
31. "The seventh from Adam" (Jude 1:14)
33. Treaties
34. Current episode of *I Love Lucy*
35. Maine college town
37. "___ ye in at the strait gate" (Matthew 7:13)
41. How Jesus often referred to himself, with "the"
44. Be fussy
48. Like the lights on Broadway
50. Stage prompt
52. Code

54. "... and all the ___ thereof shall be burned" (Micah 1:7)
55. Meaningless
56. Choir member
58. Inits. on vitamin bottles
60. Part of TNT
61. "... as a ___ doth gather her brood" (Luke 13:34)
62. At first, Samuel thought he was called by him (1 Samuel 3:5–8)
63. "A prophet is not without honour, but ... among his own ___" (Mark 6:4)
64. Great Plains Indian

1	2	3	4	■	5	6	7	8	■	9	10	11	12	13
14				■	15				■	16				
17				■	18				19					
20				21		■	22				■	■	■	■
23						24	■	25			26	27	28	29
■	■	■	30				31	■	32					
33	34	35		■	36			37	■	38				
39				■	40				41	■	42			
43				44	■	45				■	46			
47					48	■	49			50		■	■	■
51						52	■	53				54	55	56
■	■	■	■	57			58	■	59					
60	61	62	63					64		■	65			
66					■	67				■	68			
69					■	70				■	71			

Bible Burgs

Across

1. Adam and Eve raised him (Genesis 4:1)
5. Deny oneself, as Jesus did in the wilderness (Matthew 4:2)
9. Prince of India
14. Cry of frustration
15. Canyon sound
16. Tare sower, in a parable (Matthew 13:25)
17. Town where Jesus was born (Luke 2:4–7)
19. Electronic info source
20. Uncooked
21. Stays with, as the Comforter (John 14:16)
23. A flattering mouth works this, in Proverbs 26:28
24. Peter, Paul, and others
26. Hails from Caesar
28. Clairvoyant
29. Shrewd manager in a parable (Luke 16:1–8)
32. Jesus called the Father this (Mark 14:36)
35. In the vicinity
36. Actress Thompson of *Back to the Future*
37. Chinese author and evangelist
38. Town where Jesus raised Lazarus (John 11)
41. Finish
42. Part of Peter's fishing gear (Luke 5:2–3)
43. "Tree of knowledge of good and ___" (Genesis 2:9)
44. Book after Joel
45. Second son of Joseph (Genesis 41:52)
47. *90210* actress Spelling
50. Transmitted
51. Philip's wife (Matthew 14:3)
55. Respond like John the Baptist in the womb (Luke 1:41)
57. Lack of vitality
59. Long-distance inits.
60. Visitor from Venus
62. Town where Jesus healed Peter's mother-in-law (Matthew 8:5–15)
64. "I ___ do it!"
65. Memo header (abbr)
66. Prefix meaning "soil"
67. The wages of sin (Romans 6:23)
68. Rt. hand man
69. Downright nasty

Down

1. Hooded snake
2. "You're in ___ of trouble!"
3. How Solomon said to divide a child (1 Kings 3:25)
4. Japanese drama
5. "All hands shall be ___, and all knees shall be weak" (Ezekiel 7:17)
6. More painful
7. Outbuildings
8. Big book
9. Kind of room or center (abbr)
10. Brother of 54-Down (Matthew 4:18)
11. City where young Jesus spoke in the temple (Luke 2:42)
12. Mine, in Montreal
13. Song at the Last Supper (Matthew 26:30)
18. After curfew
22. Jesus told him, "Get thee behind me" (Luke 4:8)
25. FICA funds it
27. Extremely
29. Dead or Red follower
30. Nevada city
31. Partners of moms
32. Diarist Frank
33. Pager signal
34. Town that Jesus rebuked with Chorazin (Luke 10:13)
35. Bobby Orr's org.

38. Massachusetts town, slang
39. "Don't Cry for Me, Argentina" musical
40. Allen of *Home Improvement*
44. Lend a hand
46. Turn to the Lord (Luke 13:3)
47. Encourages to sin
48. Set straight
49. Surf sound
51. Preliminary races
52. Graven idol (Exodus 20:4)
53. Japanese automaker
54. Peter's other name (Luke 5:8)
55. Alan or Cheryl
56. Peace Nobelist Wiesel
58. March tourney sponsor (abbr)
61. Ultimate degree
63. *Miss Saigon* setting, briefly

1	2	3	4	■	5	6	7	8	■	9	10	11	12	13
14				■	15				■	16				
17				18					■	19				
20			■	21					22	■	23			
24			25					■	26	27			■	■
■	■	■	28				■	29					30	31
32	33	34		■	■	■	35				■	36		
37			■	38	39	40					■	41		
42			■	43				■	■	■	44			
45			46				■	47	48	49		■	■	■
■	■	50				■	51					52	53	54
55	56			■	57	58					■	59		
60				61	■	62					63			
64					■	65				■	66			
67					■	68				■	69			

Clothes Calls

Across

1. Those chosen by God (Matthew 24:31)
6. Esther's people (Esther 4:13)
10. Flat-bottomed boat
14. The Pentateuch
15. Touched down
16. Water-to-wine town (John 2:1–11)
17. With 36-Across, garment that Israel gave to Joseph (Genesis 37:3)
19. Mingo portrayer Ed
20. ___ *Pinafore*
21. Track events
22. It's all grass, to Isaiah (Isaiah 40:6)
23. Bel ___ cheese
24. Songwriter Jacques
25. Best number of golf strokes
28. Beatitude opener (Matthew 5:3–11)
31. Cowardly lion portrayer
32. Talent hunter
34. Cable movie channel (abbr)
35. "___ tu" (Verdi aria)
36. See 17-Across
38. Atmospheric prefix
39. Bar assoc. member
40. Praying figure
41. Business partnership
42. Hometown of Abimelech (Judges 8:31)
44. "Ye are our epistle written in our ___" (2 Corinthians 3:2)
46. Prefix with flow
47. Graven images
49. Embellish
51. Squash or pumpkin
52. ___-mo replay
55. Netanyahu, informally
56. David danced before the ark wearing this (1 Chronicles 15:27)
58. Adam's wife, and namesakes
59. "Don't bet ___!"
60. 18 holes, for example
61. At the end of the line
62. Snack in a shell
63. Makes a joyful noise, perhaps (Psalm 100:1)

Down

1. Inscribe with acid
2. Hover threateningly
3. Timeline divisions
4. One of Daniel's den "pets," for example (Daniel 6:16)
5. Doubting apostle (John 20:24–25)
6. Brother of John (Acts 12:2)
7. Put in seventh heaven
8. Takes home the gold
9. Swine's confines
10. Fish must have these to be clean (Leviticus 11:12)
11. Material for John's clothing (Mark 1:6)
12. Dollar bills
13. Clean up
18. Shake the dust off of them (Mark 6:11)
22. Worries
23. Part of mph
24. Become fuzzy
25. Dog biters
26. Creation in Genesis 1:1
27. Martyrs' clothing (Revelation 6:11)
28. Boxer's fight
29. Film critic Roger
30. College lodgings
32. Sound of an angry exit
33. Sentence server
36. "Suzanne" songwriter Leonard
37. Cookie
41. Mis' followers
43. Peter recognized Jesus as this (Matthew 16:16)
44. Antelope feature
45. Synagogue leaders
47. Greek column style
48. Because of
49. Cain's brother (Genesis 4:1–2)
50. Opera figure
51. Actress Lollobrigida
52. Give the cold shoulder to
53. Word before shot or division
54. Factor in decision making
56. He fled from Sodom (Genesis 19)
57. Luau dish

1	2	3	4	5	■	6	7	8	9	■	10	11	12	13
14					■	15				■	16			
17					18					■	19			
20			■	21					■	22				
■	■	■	23					■	24				■	■
25	26	27				■	■	28					29	30
31				■	■	32	33				■	34		
35			■	36	37						■	38		
39			■	40					■	■	41			
42			43				■	■	44	45				
■	■	46				■	47	48				■	■	■
49	50				■	51					■	52	53	54
55				■	56						57			
58				■	59				■	60				
61				■	62				■	63				

Read All About It

Across

1. VCR button
5. Ali ___ and the 40 Thieves
9. Gown
14. Monarch's job
15. State openly
16. The bucking stops here
17. The "U" in I.C.U.
18. Aria, e.g.
19. Li'l one
20. Biblical headline (1 Samuel 17:49–51)
23. Bard's before
24. Parted sea (Exodus 13:18; 14:21)
25. Heavy weight
26. Opposite of fast
27. First garden (Genesis 2:8)
29. Qualified number cruncher (abbr)
32. Fierce fish
35. Prayer closer
36. Plane, e.g.
37. Biblical headline (Exodus 14:22)
40. Minable minerals
41. Polite interruption
42. Lightbulb units
43. Dripping
44. Terrier type
45. It's frequently 72
46. Gobbled up
47. Order between ready and fire
48. Pie ___ mode
51. Biblical headline (Judges 16:21)
57. Once more
58. Nick Charles' wife
59. Des Moines is its capital
60. Scold
61. Web conversation
62. Bleak
63. Comic Soupy
64. "Where the heart is"
65. Pianist Myra

Down

1. Goody-goody
2. Before orbiter or rover
3. Breathing
4. Abominable Snowman
5. "Saul Escapes Damascus in a ___!" (Acts 9:25)
6. Sidestep
7. ___ weevil
8. Military no-show
9. "Michael and Angels Fight ___!" (Revelation 12:7)
10. Batman's sidekick
11. Poet ___ St.Vincent Millay
12. Spotted
13. Prepare laundry, perhaps
21. Explorer Sir Francis
22. Dictation taker, short
26. Flubs
27. Host
28. Skin: suffix
29. Price
30. Meter maker
31. Word of woe
32. ___ and tell
33. Roll call answer
34. Help a hoodlum
35. Grayish
36. Peter or Ivan, e.g.
38. Greet the day
39. Indian teacher
44. "Joshua Sets 12 Memorial ___!" (Joshua 4:20)
45. "___ Releases Barabbas!" (Mark 15:15)
46. Parenthetical comment
47. Sarai's husband (Genesis 11:31)
48. Worship
49. *Chronicles of Narnia* author
50. Revolutionary leader Samuel
51. Small pouches
52. Turkish chief
53. Post
54. Foot division
55. London district
56. Near

1	2	3	4	■	5	6	7	8	■	9	10	11	12	13
14				■	15				■	16				
17				■	18				■	19				
20				21					22					
23			■	24			■	■	25			■	■	■
■	■	■	26			■	27	28			■	29	30	31
32	33	34			■	35				■	36			
37					38					39				
40				■	41				■	42				
43			■	44				■	45			■	■	■
■	■	■	46			■	■	47			■	48	49	50
51	52	53				54	55				56			
57					■	58				■	59			
60					■	61				■	62			
63					■	64				■	65			

Plants in the Plan

Across

1. Restaurant bill, informally
4. Syrup sources
10. Drowsiness shall clothe a man with these (Proverbs 23:21)
14. "Do not ___, my beloved brethren" (James 1:16)
15. Feature of a phonograph record
16. Toast topper
17. Many a CEO has one
18. Have faith the size of this (Luke 17:6)
20. It's "brought down to the grave," according to Isaiah 14:11
22. Ran into
23. "If I ___ but touch his garment . . ." (Matthew 9:21)
24. Earth's path
26. "And this I ___ the gospel's sake . . ." (1 Corinthians 9:23)
28. Like the figs that could not be eaten (Jeremiah 24:2)
31. The lame man shall do this "as a hart" (Isaiah 35:6)
33. Formerly
35. Bullfight cry
37. He was once known as Simon
40. Hinder
41. Place for a ring, maybe
43. Cleanse, as with hyssop (Psalm 51:7)
45. Volcano in Sicily
46. Obeys the instruction to the Gentiles, in Romans 15:11
48. Ruth's mother-in-law
50. Contractor's quote (abbr)
51. Being risked
53. Skyrocket
55. "Quiet!"
56. Farm buildings
59. Church escort
62. Tofu base
63. Giant Mel of Cooperstown
65. Big rig
66. Look for this in the wilderness (Isaiah 41:19)
71. "Too cool!"
72. Game for the horsey set
73. A martial art
74. Large
75. Dog's sharp bark
76. Stockholm's land
77. Wily

Down

1. Musical pace
2. Ann ___, Michigan
3. Don't gather grapes from this (Luke 6:44)
4. *Singing in the Rain* movie studio (abbr)
5. Calla lily family
6. Sat for a painting
7. Game of chance (abbr)
8. A Gabor
9. "The ___ on the Mount"
10. Optimistic
11. Pub order
12. "Golly!"
13. Make a lawn
19. Emulated those who would die for a good man (Romans 5:7)
21. Easy dessert
25. Faucet
27. Do without
28. Eat some with unleavened bread (Exodus 12:8)
29. Words ending all four Gospels
30. Emulate the Pied Piper
32. Get up and go
34. Golfer's gadget
35. Pueblo cooking pots
36. Reluctant (to)
38. Piano adjuster

39. Important time
42. Summer hrs. in New York
44. Printer's measures
47. Wooden shoe
49. Debtor's letters
52. Skin-covered canoes
54. Balaam's spoke (Numbers 22:28)
57. University of ___ Dame
58. Pricey violin, briefly
60. Send via computer
61. Like some mountain ranges
62. " . . . no man shall ___ me of this boasting" (2 Corinthians 11:10)
64. Head: Fr.
66. Joshua sent two men to do this (Joshua 2:1)
67. Garden tool
68. What it shall be with the wicked (Isaiah 3:11)
69. *Hee-*___
70. Nightfall, poetically

1	2	3	■	4	5	6	7	8	9	■	10	11	12	13
14			■	15						■	16			
17			■	18						19				
20			21	■	22			■	23			■	■	■
24				25	■	26		27			■	28	29	30
■	■	31			32	■	■	33			34			
35	36		■	37		38	39		■	40				
41			42	■	43				44	■	45			
46				47	■	48				49	■	50		
51					52		■	■	53		54		■	■
55			■	56			57	58	■	59			60	61
■	■	■	62			■	63		64	■	65			
66	67	68				69				70	■	71		
72				■	73						■	74		
75				■	76						■	77		

ANGLING WITH ANGELS

Across

1. Omega counterpart (Revelation 1:8)
6. Tribe that kept the tabernacle (Numbers 1:50)
10. "Gee whillikers!"
14. Potential pruning hook (Isaiah 2:4)
15. Philbrick's ___ *Three Lives*
16. Needing a massage
17. Prayer of David
18. Type of club
19. Dire destiny
20. Evangelists in Matthew 4:19
23. Substance-approving agcy.
26. Tennis court divider
27. Do this to those who curse you (Matthew 5:44)
28. God (Psalm 46:1)
30. Jesus drove out the changers of this (John 2:15)
33. Minor prophet
34. Senate spots
35. Architect I. M. ___
38. With 53-Across, the Spirit's instructions on evangelism and sanctification?
42. Weekend TV fare
43. Kind of fairy
44. "What's ___ you?"
45. North Pole dweller
46. Prophet with cats in the den
48. Tower of confusion (Genesis 11:9)
51. One path to the www
52. Surgery sites (abbr)
53. See 38-Across
58. *All in the Family* producer Norman
59. Ruth's homeland (Ruth 1:4)
60. Harlot of Jericho (Joshua 6:17)
64. Gospel after Mark
65. Actress Swenson
66. Reuben, for one (Numbers 1:5)
67. Proofreader's "leave it"
68. Keep the Fourth Commandment (Exodus 20:8)
69. Sport with clay pigeons

Down

1. Snake that doesn't hurt a child (Isaiah 11:8)
2. Music collectibles (abbr)
3. Soup legume
4. Radius, to diameter
5. Giving weapons to
6. It shines in the darkness (John 1:5)
7. Fashion mag
8. Go in a new direction
9. Fateful March day
10. Annoying sort
11. Invitation to worship (Psalm 95:6)
12. Moses took them off before the burning bush (Exodus 3:5)
13. Spiritual songs (Colossians 3:16)
21. "Told ya!"
22. More than chubby
23. Brawls
24. Devil, in the NRSV (Matthew 7:22)
25. Run ___ of
29. The Trojans of the NCAA
30. Conductor Zubin
31. Scout's recitation
32. Utmost degree
34. Kilt wearer, short
35. Outdoor sitting area
36. "___ into his gates with thanksgiving" (Psalm 100:4)
37. Second Commandment taboo in NRSV (Exodus 20:4)
39. To any extent
40. 32,000 ounces
41. Max. opposite
45. Like hidden faults (Psalm 19:12)
46. *The Simpsons* outburst
47. Gives a heads-up to
48. Congress votes on them
49. Alaskan tongue
50. "The Tyger" poet William
51. Ready to hit
54. Islamic ruler
55. Primo
56. Complains continuously
57. Gospel after Matthew
61. Hurry, to Shakespeare
62. Presidential namesake of a patriarch (Hebrews 7:4)
63. Take a chance

1	2	3	4	5	■	6	7	8	9	■	10	11	12	13
14					■	15				■	16			
17					■	18				■	19			
■	■	■	20		21					22				
23	24	25	■	26			■	■	■	27				
28			29			■	30	31	32			■	■	■
33				■	■	34					■	35	36	37
38				39	40						41			
42			■	43					■	■	44			
■	■	■	45					■	46	47				
48	49	50			■	■	■	51			■	52		
53					54	55	56				57	■	■	■
58				■	59				■	60		61	62	63
64				■	65				■	66				
67				■	68				■	69				

Three of Egypt's Plagues

Across

1. Noah's oldest son (Genesis 6:10)
5. Book before Philemon
10. Philippian lodging for Paul (Acts 16:23)
14. Taylor of *Mystic Pizza*
15. Archie Bunker's wife
16. Prefix with potent or present
17. "Feudin' with ___"
18. Mount of the Ten Commandments (Exodus 31:18)
19. Extremely, before "afraid" (Luke 2:9)
20. White House tune, a plague (Exodus 9:22)
23. Bro's counterpart
24. Moo ___ pork
25. Experience, as death, with "of" (Matthew 16:28)
28. "The fool hath said... There is no ___" (Psalm 14:1)
31. The dry land, in Genesis 1:10
35. Where to look, in "Misty"
36. Add water to
38. Classified ad acknowledgment
39. Conrad novel, a plague (Exodus 10:21)
42. Anointing fluid of Psalm 23:5
43. Sensory membrane
44. Patmos, for example (Revelation 1:9)
45. Zhou ___
47. Idols cannot do this (Psalm 135:16)
48. Place
49. Neither
51. Psychic's ability (abbr)
52. Slow mail delivery in a rhyme, a plague (Exodus 8:5)
60. Subject of the "new commandment" in John 13:34
61. King of Judea when the King of kings was born (Matthew 2:1)
62. He killed his brother (Genesis 4:8)
64. He was killed by his brother (Genesis 4:8)
65. Cable channel
66. Metric weight unit
67. Ink dispensers
68. Like the way to destruction (Matthew 7:13)
69. Symbol of forgiven sins (Isaiah 1:18)

Down

1. Patty Hearst's kidnappers (abbr)
2. "... a throne, ___ and lifted up" (Isaiah 6:1)
3. *On the Waterfront* director Kazan
4. Attend, as angels did to Jesus (Matthew 4:11)
5. Dry runs
6. Prefix meaning "personal"
7. Windshield feature
8. Great Salt Lake site
9. Acts skittish
10. Nun's son (Numbers 14:30)
11. Mine, to Marcel
12. Memo opener
13. Gladly
21. Break the Ninth Commandment (Exodus 20:16)
22. If hit here, don't hit back (Luke 6:29)
25. Resort lake
26. Had a home-cooked meal
27. Back part
28. Prophecy, tongues, healing, etc. (1 Corinthians 12:1–11)
29. "___ but goodie"
30. One of the Allman Brothers
32. Della of *Touched by an Angel*
33. Edison contemporary
34. Sprayed
36. Deer mom

37. Refrain syllable
40. Peter, Paul, and Mary and others
41. Strains at a gnat (Matthew 23:24)
46. Gabriel and Michael
48. Nine-digit no. issuer
50. Jericho woman who helped the Israelites (Joshua 6:17)
51. Came to a close
52. What flags do in the wind
53. Scarlet garment of the Passion (Matthew 27:28)
54. Bakery fixture
55. Close
56. Foe of James Bond
57. Fizzy drink
58. Stretched out
59. Grain holder
63. "The hour cometh, and ___ is, when the true worshippers . . ." (John 4:23)

1	2	3	4		5	6	7	8	9		10	11	12	13
14					15						16			
17					18						19			
	20			21						22				
			23						24					
25	26	27				28	29	30		31		32	33	34
35					36				37			38		
39				40							41			
42				43							44			
45			46			47				48				
			49		50				51					
52	53	54				55	56	57				58	59	
60					61						62			63
64					65						66			
67					68						69			

Bible Fauna

Across

1. Wool growers (Mark 6:34)
6. Graceful white bird (Leviticus 11:18)
10. Health resorts
14. Luminous radiances
15. Singer Perry
16. Whip mark
17. ___ firma
18. Black-and-white cookie
19. Large constellation
20. Butterfly-to-be (Isaiah 33:4)
23. Forbidden antelope (Deuteronomy 14:5)
27. Aerodynamically designed
28. Slim down
29. Reach
32. On a whim
33. Nature's soil aerator
37. Finish first
38. Fire-starting rock
39. Playwright Akins
40. Desert stingers (Deuteronomy 8:15)
43. Push roughly
45. Refuge
46. Upright piano
47. Loathe
50. Eager dam builders
51. Crop-destroying insect (Judges 6:5)
55. Dryer leftover
56. Spoken
57. Poe's bird (Genesis 8:7)
62. Woodwind instrument
63. Lima's land
64. Mediterranean oil
65. Small dam
66. Moose kin
67. Helped with the dishes

Down

1. "So Jonah went out of the city. . . and ___ on the east side of the city" (Jonah 4:5)
2. Companion of cry
3. "To ___ is human"
4. Lobe site
5. Showy zoo strutter (Job 39:13)
6. Aberdonians
7. Had on
8. Uncle Sam's country (abbr)
9. NASA's do-nothing
10. Fork-tailed songbird (Proverbs 26:2)
11. Hostess Mesta
12. Aquarium growth
13. Baby bird
21. Government agency in Australia (abbr)
22. Narrow strip of land (abbr)
23. Bird crops
24. Spiral-shaped
25. *A Bell for* ___
26. Adrienne's wall
29. Increases
30. White-tailed sea eagles
31. E-mail from youngster to youngster (abbr)
33. Jesus' cry from the cross (Mark 15:34)
34. Endangered atmospheric gas
35. Apollo's lunar vehicle
36. Tournaments
38. Hi and sci
41. Barnyard's alarm clock (Mark 14:72 NIV)
42. Bogey beaters
43. Finch (Proverbs 26:2 NRSV)
44. AIDS virus

46. Catch on
47. Beaming
48. Hush money
49. Vietnam capital
50. Better than average grade
52. Funnyman Bob
53. Russian city
54. Establish a satellite in orbit
58. "Greatest" ring king
59. Celeb
60. First lady (Genesis 3:20)
61. *Waking ___ Devine*

KINSWOMAN

Across

1. "___ was in the days of my youth" (Job 29:4)
4. 1970s dance craze
9. Single-cell organisms
16. There was no room in one (Luke 2:7)
17. China
18. Russian ballerina Anna
19. Actor Stephen of *In Dreams*
20. "...and on his thigh ___ written" (Revelation 19:16)
21. A kinswoman's greeting: Part 1 (Luke 1:42)
22. Intoxicate
24. Dabbling duck
26. In actual existence
27. Greeting, Part 2
30. Manner of walking
31. An alum probably has one
32. Writer Upton of *The Jungle*
38. Job's was heavier than his groaning (Job 23:2)
40. "If I may be so bold..."
42. "Get thee ___, Satan" (Matthew 4:10)
43. "...___ is of the truth." (1 John 2:21)
45. Like the ink in Rorschach tests
47. Greeting, Part 3
51. Most cautious
52. V-formation flyers
53. "...___ well?" (Naaman's question to Gehazi, 2 Kings 5:21)
54. "Therefore take ___ to your spirit" (Malachi 2:15)
56. Slept noisily
61. Willy Loman and others
63. Service charge
65. Florida county
66. Greeting, Part 4
69. Home to Cornell University
74. "Who his own ___ bare our sins" (1 Peter 2:24)
75. "___ as a seal upon thine heart" (Song 8:6)
76. Greeting, Part 5
78. Start of the Hebrew alphabet
80. Vietnam Veterans Memorial designer
81. Pleasure-seeking
82. Musical actress Lenya
83. UFO pilots (abbr)
84. Like Samson, after the Philistines captured him
85. "...ye shall not ___ by my name falsely" (Leviticus 19:12)
86. Get the picture

Down

1. Car safety devices
2. Show disdain for
3. All atwitter
4. What Jesus was condemned to
5. Writer Fleming
6. Michelangelo's "David," for one
7. "Huh?"
8. Time for a refrigerator raid, maybe
9. NYPD alert
10. Speak evil of
11. Baking chamber mentioned four times in Leviticus
12. Otherwise
13. Head honcho
14. Roman greetings
15. "Smooth Operator" singer
23. Holy Roman Emperor known as "The Great"
25. "A time to get, a time to ___..." (Ecclesiastes 3:6)
28. Old Greek theaters
29. Like candlestick-jumping Jack, in a rhyme
33. Like the Israelites, according to Deuteronomy
34. Response to "Shall we?"
35. Feed the kitty
36. Chilled
37. A primary color
39. Prepares to pray, perhaps
41. Row of shrubbery
44. Wood-shaping machines
46. Like the "light to rule the night" (Genesis 1:16)
47. "Certainly, this ___ righteous man." (Luke 23:47)

48. By mouth
49. 1,760 yards
50. Political ally
51. Dairy state (abbr)
55. Tolkien creatures
57. Garfield's housemate
58. Baby's toys
59. "He is thy brother" (Deuteronomy 23:7)
60. Protection
62. Native Americans originally from the Green Bay area
64. Weak or delicate
67. Cures
68. In a theater or church
69. ". . . for ___ Lord thy God am a jealous God" (Exodus 20:5)
70. "Blessed are ___ that mourn" (Matthew 5:4)
71. Jekyll's alter ego
72. Off base
73. Edible ice cream holder
77. Yrs. prior to the birth of Jesus
79. Sch. bake sale org.

HIDDEN WORD

Across

1. Removes reminders of mortality from the furniture
6. John and James left them to follow Jesus (Matthew 4:21–22)
11. Mary's mourning over Jesus depiction
16. Begin beginning (Genesis 1:1)
17. Zhou ___
18. Hummingbirds do it
19. Fifth wheel
20. Slightest
21. Like a silly comedy routine
22. Bible book hiding a word for "defeat"
24. Created on the third day (Genesis 1:11)
25. British weapon
26. Scot. var. of self
27. Dangerous part of a sword
29. Transatlantic flyer (abbr)
30. "I'm all ___"
32. Sparkles
34. Break down grammatically
37. Jam or pickle
38. Chilled
42. Reverent respect
43. Human-looking machine
46. They threw Jezebel out the window (2 Kings 9:30–33)
48. Eat pasta, with "up"
50. Bible book hiding a word for "devoid of emotion"
52. Horse's trot
53. Don't blow it when you give
55. Speak
57. SSW's opposite
58. Mister in Spanish
59. Della Reese's angel role
61. Where Paul read "To an unknown God" (Acts 17:23)
63. Social harmony
65. Enc. in an envelope
67. Tie the knot
70. Jesus, to the branches (John 15:5)
71. From ___ Z
72. Sticky sealer
76. "___ knew you; depart from me" (Matthew 7:23)
78. Bible book hiding a word for "bliss"
81. To date
82. Where Mother Teresa worked
83. Send in
84. Going to Nineveh, for Jonah
85. Suez waterway
86. Tape deck button
87. Stuffs to the gills
88. Units within tribes
89. Flower with rays

Down

1. They go into drives
2. Prepare to transplant
3. Like cut-rate bread
4. Supporters of the kings of Israel
5. Looks
6. Contradicts
7. Cager Shaq
8. Arkin or Alda
9. Israelite cloak attachments
10. Warm the bench
11. Bible book hiding a word for a citrus fruit
12. College in New Rochelle, NY
13. Maurice of *Bewitched*
14. Army shelters
15. "Give it ___!"
23. On outdated maps (abbr)
24. Tiger's org.
28. Where streams break out for Isaiah (Isaiah 35:6)
31. Prefix for atmosphere
32. "Hop to it!"
33. All cozy
34. Covenants
35. In the know
36. Old fare on the air
37. Elizabeth, to John, familiarly (Luke 1:57–60)
39. Defeatist's words
40. Company dinnerware
41. Banana oil, for example
44. Number of the ten lepers that thanked Jesus (Luke 17:15)
45. Be nosy

47. Milk, so to speak
49. U. Hotshot
51. Pl. suffix for small one
54. Bible book hiding a word for "verify"
56. Dormitory VIPs
60. Word before life or fire
62. Romans and others
64. Former Russian space station
65. Violates the eighth commandment (Exodus 20:15)
66. One path to the www
67. Faint traces
68. Name on a bomber
69. Make more lean
71. For the birds
73. Get a bead on
74. Modeling asset
75. "___ into his gates with thanksgiving" (Psalm 100:4)
77. Wind instrument
79. Ferber of *Show Boat*
80. Geometry calculation
82. Trade watchdog (abbr)

1	2	3	4	5	■	6	7	8	9	10	■	11	12	13	14	15
16					■	17					■	18				
19					■	20					■	21				
22					23					■	24					
25				■	26			■	27	28			■	29		
■	■	■	30	31			■	32					33	■	■	■
34	35	36			■	■	37				■	38		39	40	41
42			■	43	44	45			■	46	47					
48			49	■	50				51			■	52			
53				54			■	55				56	■	57		
58					■	59	60			■	■	61	62			
■	■	■	63		64				■	65	66			■	■	■
67	68	69	■	70				■	71			■	72	73	74	75
76			77			■	78	79				80				
81					■	82					■	83				
84					■	85					■	86				
87					■	88					■	89				

Dynamic Duos

Across

1. Begot
6. Split down the middle
12. Small clump
16. "And they were exceeding sorrowful, and began every one of them to say unto him, Lord, ___?" (Matthew 26:22)
17. Real estate account
18. Fit for duty
19. In-laws (Ruth 1:22)
21. "Thou knowest my downsitting and mine uprising, thou understandest my thought ___ off." (Psalm 139:2)
22. Fast-acting
23. In good shape
24. Dada pioneer Jean
25. *Waiting to Exhale* actress Rochon
27. Quito's country (abbr)
29. Pop singer Vannelli
30. Track circuit
33. Brothers (Exodus 4:14)
36. Checkout scanner (abbr)
37. Diarist Anaïs
38. Bring home
39. Damsel who answered Peter's knock at the gate after his release from prison (Acts 12:13)
42. Bee Gees surname
45. Marsh plant
48. Adulterers (2 Samuel 11:2–4)
52. Copier powder
53. Calcutta cover-up
54. Fork parts
55. On the safe side
57. "___ a bird"
59. A captain in David's army (1 Chronicles 27:9)
60. Sisters and rival wives (Genesis 29—30)
66. UFO passengers
67. Corrida cries
68. *The Clan of the Cave Bear* author
69. Holiday preceders
71. Coq au ___
72. 451, in old Rome
74. "He that ___ of this bread shall live for ever." (John 6:58)
78. Old flames
80. Twins (Genesis 25:21–26)
82. Hamm and Farrow
83. Unkeyed, in music
84. Repasts
85. Formerly, formerly
86. Passover dinners
87. *Love Story* novelist Segal

Down

1. "And brought them out, and said, ___, what must I do to be saved?" (Acts 16:30)
2. "The jig ___!"
3. Religious ceremony
4. Lucy's landlady
5. "Thou shalt also be a crown of glory in the hand of the Lord, and a royal ___ in the hand of thy God." (Isaiah 62:3)
6. "Jesus saith unto him, Rise, take up thy ___, and walk." (John 5:8)
7. Does not exist
8. Spooks
9. Beethoven's Symphony No. 3
10. "Stand in awe, and sin not: ___ with your own heart upon your bed, and be still." (Psalm 4:4)
11. Light starter
12. Alta or Baja in Puerto Rico
13. Not equitable
14. "Yea, though I walk through the valley of the shadow of death, I will ___ evil" (Psalm 23:4)
15. Atlantic game fish
20. Hosiery material
26. "Therefore the Lord himself shall give you ___; Behold, a virgin shall conceive, and bear a son, and shall call his name Immanuel." (Isaiah 7:14)
28. Make ___ for it (race)
29. Indira of India
30. Jehovah
31. Have ___ with (speak to)
32. Brigham Young University site
34. Writers Bagnold and Blyton
35. "There remaineth therefore ___ to the people of God." (Hebrews 4:9)
40. "... two of the sons of Jacob, Simeon and Levi, ___ brethren,

took each man his sword, and came upon the city boldly, and slew all the males." (Genesis 34:25)

41. Writer Rogers St. John

43. Bus. degree

44. Relating to atmospheric pressure

46. *Arabian Nights* character

47. Film critic Roger

49. Sphere of interest

50. "Thou shalt truly ___ all the increase of thy seed, that the field bringeth forth year by year." (Deuteronomy 14:22)

51. "Nevertheless ___ heart was perfect with the Lord all his days." (1 Kings 15:14)

56. Show the ropes

58. "___ days shall ye eat unleavened bread" (Exodus 12:15)

60. "If ye ___, keep my commandments." (John 14:15)

61. Touted cure-all

62. Man sick of the palsy who was healed by Peter (Acts 9:34)

63. Saltwater fish native to New Zealand

64. The same/Of no importance

65. "Teach me thy way, O Lord, and ___ in a plain path, because of mine enemies." (Psalm 27:11)

70. Turn the helm

73. Construction beam

75. Morales of *La Bamba*

76. Bath powder

77. "Quiet!"

79. Jet set jet (abbr)

80. Madison or Monroe (abbr)

81. Capp and Capone

1	2	3	4	5	■	6	7	8	9	10	11	■	12	13	14	15
16					■	17						■	18			
19					20							■	21			
22						■	23				■	■	■	24		
■	■	■	25			26	■	27			28	■	29			
30	31	32	■	33			34					35				
36			■	■	37			■	■	38				■	■	■
39			40	41	■	42		43	44	■	45			46	47	■
48					49					50						51
■	52					■	53				■	54				
■	■	■	55			56	■	■	57		58	■	■	59		
60	61	62					63	64				65	■	66		
67				■	68				■	69			70	■	■	■
71			■	■	■	72			73	■	74			75	76	77
78			79	■	80					81						
82				■	83						■	84				
85				■	86						■	87				

Famous Phrases

Across

1. Not so precarious
6. Knocked off, to Cain (Genesis 4:8)
10. Biblical crib substitute (Luke 2:12)
16. Emulate Cicero
17. Garr of *Mr. Mom*
18. Pass by
19. Bathsheba's husband (2 Samuel 11:3)
20. Follows John
21. Blown by winds of doctrine (James 1:6)
22. Righteous people (Matthew 5:13)
25. Positive votes (var)
26. U. degrees
27. Kind of jacket
28. Mil. jet locale
31. Milk producer
32. Lion's statement
34. Sound
36. Alter (Jeremiah 13:23)
39. Fairy-tale writer
41. Snake rendered harmless (Isaiah 11:8)
42. Card game
43. Western Hemisphere grp.
44. Sandwich (abbr)
45. Lawyers' org.
47. Chinese author and evangelist
48. Clothes
51. Winter road hazard
52. Pays attention to the statutes of the Lord, e.g.
54. Bounty of nature (Genesis 45:18)
58. Haunting
59. Insect wound
60. Lennon's lady
61. European eagle
62. Dress up, with "out"
63. Tack on
64. Abib and Ziv (abbr)
67. Pass away (Job 3:11)
72. Jesus cast them out (Matthew 9:33, NRSV)
75. Misty of *Hee Haw*
76. Awaken
77. When Caleb wanted to possess Canaan (Numbers 13:30)
78. *On the Waterfront* director Kazan
79. Belly button type, slang
80. Depth companion in Romans 8:39
81. "So ___ I you" (John 20:21)
82. He said, "Thou art the Christ" (Matthew 16:16)

Down

1. March composer
2. Battle formation (Jeremiah 50:42)
3. Goes under
4. "L'___ c'est moi"
5. Son of Solomon (1 Kings 11:43)
6. Baseball numbers (abbr)
7. Poland's Walesa
8. Art Deco name
9. Builder on a rock, in parable (Matthew 7:24)
10. Way around Paris
11. Oodles
12. Author Ogden
13. Luke, perhaps, and others (Colossians 4:14, abbr)
14. Diction, suffix
15. Esau's color at birth (Genesis 25:25)
23. Babe in the woods
24. Swiss river
28. Like the temple, covered with gems (Luke 21:5)
29. Made to follow contours
30. Pushes around
31. Board leader (abbr)
32. Keep the Sabbath (Exodus 35:2)
33. Alley-___
34. Enzyme, suffix
35. "There arose ___ new king" (Exodus 1:8)
36. Water source
37. Guy's honey
38. Doo-wop syllable
39. Chin adornment
40. "I had ___ be a doorkeeper" (Psalm 84:10)
44. Vegas venture
45. Pine
46. Insect image of Assyria (Isaiah 7:18)
49. "Don't mind ___ do"
50. Comedienne Charlotte
51. *The Addams Family* member
52. Handlebar part
53. Brian of rock music
55. Reed in a pit

56. Cherubim in the temple, e.g. (1 Kings 6:29)
57. Metal deposit
62. Remote target
63. In front
64. Horeb or Gilead
65. Davis of *Do the Right Thing*
66. Handle the helm
67. Game show prop
68. Rainfall measurement
69. Serpent support (Numbers 21:8)
70. Esau, to Jacob (Genesis 25:24)
71. Fine-tune
72. Long for Morse code
73. L' ___, summer in Paris
74. "Me," in Marseille

And the Hits Just Keep Coming!

Across

1. Rings
7. They "skipped . . . like lambs," in Psalm 114:6
12. Pierce
16. Abe's description
17. " . . . know that I am the Lord, the Holy ___ Israel" (Ezekiel 39:7)
18. Political patronage, slang
19. As a precaution
20. Honshu port
21. Shade trees
22. Top 40 hit for Peter and the apostles
25. German city on the Ruhr
26. Issachar was a strong one, according to Jacob (Genesis 49:14)
27. Kind of rhyme
30. E-mails, but not as the main recipient
32. What Jesus did, at the death of Lazarus (John 11:35)
33. "And ___ kingdom be divided against itself" (Mark 3:24)
34. Top 40 hit for Ruth and Naomi
40. Manually adroit
42. "Concerning," on a memo
43. Wickerwork using willow twigs
44. Floor covering
45. Finnish steam baths
47. Tablet
48. Clears the blackboard
52. There are four in Monopoly (abbr)
53. False start
55. "Who ___ the Lord's side?" (Exodus 32:26)
56. "Later!"
59. Top 40 hit for Michael and Gabriel
61. ICU hookups
62. Cereal grain
64. "Runaway" singer Shannon
65. Funeral rite
67. Here, to Yvette
69. Skim, as milk
74. Top 40 hit for Jeremiah and Nebuzar-adan
77. Honored, as an invoice
79. Helped out
80. Snare
81. Fairy-tale monster
82. Make a point
83. Cheap cigar
84. Look searchingly
85. Stops
86. Mexican misters

Down

1. Santiago's country
2. Sharpens
3. Early Peruvians
4. Lee's opponent at Gettysburg
5. Intrinsic property
6. Quip, tip, or hip follower
7. Travels by foot, with "it"
8. Smithsonian and others (abbr)
9. Jacob's first wife (Genesis 29:15–30)
10. In near mint condition
11. Buy quickly, as a bargain
12. Design criteria, briefly
13. *The Lord of the Rings* author (alt sp)
14. "I will redeem you with a stretched out ___" (Exodus 6:6)
15. There are 66 in the Bible canon (abbr)
23. Desert refuge
24. Camelot's king
28. One time rural postal inits.
29. "Yippee!"
31. What to take up, to follow Jesus (Mark 10:21)
32. Prison chief
34. Unfavorably, prefix
35. " . . . whom they slew and hanged ___ tree" (Acts 10:39)
36. Play about Capote
37. Husband to three Catherines, two Annes, and a Jane
38. Japan, to the Japanese
39. Fido's restraint
41. "Ye must be born ___." (John 3:7)
44. Go back from blonde to brunette
46. A Semitic language
49. Certain NCO
50. Letters on a help wanted ad
51. NBC weekend comedy (abbr)
54. Annulled
56. How the woman at Jacob's Well addressed Jesus (John 4:11)

57. "The mother of all living" (Genesis 3:20)
58. Attorney's honorific
59. Kingston's nation
60. Pasta specification
63. Go over and over
66. ". . . hide me ___ the shadow of thy wings" (Psalm 17:8)
67. Like some gases
68. Surrenders
70. Rocker John
71. Abstain from
72. Firefighter "Red"
73. Kinds
75. Elijah helped show Jezebel's to be a fake (1 Kings 18:20–40)
76. Military dining area
77. Dad
78. Elisabeth "conceived a son in her old ___." (Luke 1:36)

1	2	3	4	5	6	■	7	8	9	10	11	■	12	13	14	15
16						■	17					■	18			
19						■	20					■	21			
22						23						24			■	■
25					■	26			■	27					28	29
■	■	■	■	30	31		■	■	32				■	33		
34	35	36	37				38	39			■	40	41			
42				■	43					■	44			■	■	■
45				46		■	47			■	48			49	50	51
■	■	■	52			■	53			54		■	55			
56	57	58			■	59						60				
61			■	62	63			■	■	64			■	■	■	■
65			66				■	67	68		■	69	70	71	72	73
■	■	74					75				76					
77	78			■	79					■	80					
81				■	82					■	83					
84				■	85					■	86					

Gospel Writers

Across

1. Not a horse or donkey (pl)
6. "The devil led him up to ___ place and showed him in an instant all the kingdoms of the world" (Luke 4:5 NIV)
11. Recedes
15. Informal evening
16. Actress Braga of *Kiss of the Spider Woman*
17. Calcutta cover-up
18. *Friends* actor
20. "___ thou mine eyes, that I may behold wondrous things out of thy law" (Psalm 119:18)
21. ___-cone
22. "He planteth an ___, and the rain doth nourish it" (Isaiah 44:14)
23. Fateful day for Caesar
25. ___ Aviv
26. High jinks
29. Take a big step
31. "Blessed be the Lord God of Israel from everlasting to everlasting: and let all the people say, ___" (Psalm 106:48)
34. "...an excellent spirit was in him; and the king thought to set him over the whole ___" (Daniel 6:3)
37. Moves like the Blob
38. Economic analysts
42. Book size
43. "...and ___ the lintel and the two side posts with the blood that is in the basin" (Exodus 12:22)
44. Formerly known as
45. "For there ___ power but of God" (Romans 13:1)
48. Old Testament prophet
49. ___ carte
52. Scumbag
54. Hoffman of *Rain Man*
56. Unenthusiastic reaction
61. Japanese dog
62. Magna ___
63. Italian hot spot
64. Gentle breeze
66. Family cars
69. "And he rested on the seventh day from ___ his work which he had made" (Genesis 2:2)
70. "But his wife looked back from behind him, and she became a pillar of ___" (Genesis 19:26)
73. Small team
74. Photo ___ (media events, abbr)
77. Tim of *Sister, Sister*
79. Viola cornuta
83. Forearm bone
84. "...for ___, and a tooth for..." (Matthew 5:38)
85. G.I. Joe's group
86. Pts. of a line
87. Physical strength
88. "Later!"

Down

1. Bewail
2. "Salvation belongeth ___ the Lord" (Psalm 3:8)
3. Ignited
4. A leader of the temple music appointed by David (1 Chronicles 15:16–19)
5. "___ thou how faith wrought with his works, and by works was faith made perfect?" (James 2:22)
6. Nile serpent
7. Clod buster
8. Cross inscription (Luke 23:38, abbr)
9. "Rend your clothes, and ___ you with sackcloth, and mourn..." (2 Samuel 3:31)
10. Theater great Helen
11. 26-Down's "___ Beso"
12. "He shall ___ you with the Holy Ghost" (Matthew 3:11)
13. Kennel club member
14. Like Christ
15. Logos (abbr)
19. Blender sound
24. Replenishes
26. Singer Paul
27. Ho-hum grade
28. Back talk
30. Architect Mies van der ___
31. Egyptian god of Thebes
32. Mugger repellent
33. Art Deco designer
35. "But ___ man examine himself," (1 Corinthians 11:28)

36. School___
39. "Turn ye from your ___, and keep my commandments" (2 Kings 17:13)
40. Put ___ (set sail)
41. ___ Janeiro
46. Drug buster
47. Baum's Emerald City princess
49. Working hard
50. "He lieth in wait secretly as a ___ in his den" (Psalm 10:9)
51. Prophetess who gave thanks for Jesus' birth (Luke 2:36–38)
52. Son of Adam (Genesis 4:25)
53. Goes astray
55. Fr. holy women
56. Jesus raised him from the dead (John 11:43–44)
57. Island strings
58. *The Jungle Book* author
59. Parisian summer
60. Golfer's aide
65. Indian chiefs
67. Meat serving, sometimes
68. Hopeless
71. Actress Anderson
72. Not now
74. Grand Ole ___
75. Big cat
76. "Moses sent them to ___ out the land of Canaan" (Numbers 13:17)
78. ___ *Kapital*
80. TV "Science Guy"
81. "O sing unto the Lord a ___ song" (Psalm 96:1)
82. Actress West

LANDMARK DECISIONS

Across

1. "Thy word is ___ unto my feet, and a light unto my path." (Psalm 119:105)
6. Deepen, as a canal
12. Gardner of Hollywood
15. Lineperson
16. All
17. Eye shade
19. Region promised to Abraham by God (Genesis 17:8)
21. Actress Chase
22. Church feature
23. Matterhorn, for one
24. Obvious flirt
25. Glowed
27. "The Lord is my ___; I shall not want." (Psalm 23:1)
29. Tail greeting
32. "And if any man hunger, let him ___ home" (1 Corinthians 11:34)
34. Purplish-gray
35. Newspaper publisher
37. Spill the beans
39. Deliberate fires
42. A body of soldiers
43. Bewitch
45. Service charge
46. "And now whereas my father did ___ you with a heavy yoke, I will add to your yoke." (1 Kings 12:11)
47. Alphabetic trio
48. Finish
49. "For ___ have many members in one body" (Romans 12:4)
50. Parisian summer
51. "The proud have hid a snare for me, and cords; they have spread a net by the ___" (Psalm 140:5)
53. Sacred song
54. Forwarded
56. ___ the line
57. Voting roster
58. Home of Stephen King's alma mater
60. Come again
62. In a pair
63. Jacob said, "The God which fed me all my ___ unto this day." (Genesis 48:15)
66. Joyous hymn
68. Regions
69. "O Lord, . . . let my ___ come unto thee." (Psalm 102:1)
71. Cast loose
75. Alan, Cheryl, or Diane
76. Peter's workplace (Matthew 4:18)
78. "___ Clock Jump" (Count Basie tune)
79. Mountain ridge where Moses died (Deuteronomy 34:1)
80. Bert's Muppet pal
81. ". . . because there was no room for them in the ___." (Luke 2:7)
82. Lend a hand
83. Croft's singing partner

Down

1. Hole punchers
2. *South Pacific* woman
3. "Rule, Britannia" composer
4. An ancient Mesopotamian people (2 Kings 18:11)
5. "For they ___ falsely unto you in my name" (Jeremiah 29:9)
6. Presentable
7. Genetic material (abbr)
8. Sicilian mount
9. Watch faces
10. Spreadsheet displays
11. Poetic dusk
12. Sets down
13. Site of the defeat of the Syrians by David's army (2 Samuel 8:13)
14. *Jeopardy!* contestant, e.g.
18. "The way of transgressors is ___." (Proverbs 13:15)
20. Parade attraction
24. Abstract art style
26. From the heart
28. African antelope
29. "God created great ___, and every living creature that moveth" (Genesis 1:21)
30. Make bubbly
31. First place (Genesis 2:8)
33. Military strategy (abbr)
36. Actress Charlotte
38. "In his hand are ___ places of the earth" (Psalm 95:4)
40. Rock bottom (with "a")

41. "If any man among you ___ be religious, and bridleth not his tongue, . . . this man's religion is vain." (James 1:26)
43. Actress Williams
44. Actress Sue ___ Langdon
47. "For other foundation ___ man lay than that is laid, which is Jesus Christ." (1 Corinthians 3:11)
49. Visual lang.
51. Cashmere and angora
52. "Therefore whether it were ___ they, so we preach, and so ye believed" (1 Corinthians 15:11)
53. Earthly stories with heavenly meanings
55. "Behold, I give unto you power to ___ serpents and scorpions" (Luke 10:19)
57. ___ Park, California
59. ___ *Not Enough* (Jacqueline Susann novel)
61. Apprehended
63. Composer Schifrin
64. Modern-day Persian
65. "If then God so clothe the ___" (Luke 12:28)
67. Bete ___ (bugbear)
70. Bear or Berra
72. Forearm bone
73. Diamond of song
74. Sandra and Ruby
76. Mineral spring
77. Mi followers

1	2	3	4	5		6	7	8	9	10	11		12	13	14	
15						16							17			18
19					20								21			
22								23				24				
			25				26		27		28					
29	30	31		32				33		34						
35			36				37		38		39				40	41
42						43				44				45		
46					47				48				49			
50				51				52				53				
54			55				56				57					
		58				59		60		61				62		
63	64						65		66				67			
68						69		70		71				72	73	74
75					76				77							
78					79							80				
	81				82							83				

Taking Flight

Across

1. Heroic tales
6. *Arabian Nights* hero
13. Sauna spot
16. Bakery lure
17. Lotion ingredient
18. ___ Aviv
19. Moses' plea to Pharaoh
21. Former California fort
22. Fish flock
23. Abu Dhabi's grp.
24. Region of Ephesus by the Aegean
26. Small batteries
27. Ones pointing fingers
30. "He shall give his ___ charge over thee, to keep thee" (Luke 4:10)
31. Prophet who rebuked Judean King Asa for siding with Syria instead of the Lord (2 Chronicles 16:7)
32. External, prefix
33. How the Lord saved the Israelites from Pharaoh's army (Exodus 14:21–30)
38. Israeli seaport
40. "Be ye not unequally ___ . . . with unbelievers" (2 Corinthians 6:14)
41. Good buddy
42. Aid in crime
43. "And Moses sent them to ___ out the land of Canaan" (Numbers 13:17)
46. Double curve
47. Tenure in office
48. Ignited
49. Impish
51. Doctorate exams
52. Meal that commemorates Israel's deliverance from bondage
57. "___ therefore God hath joined together, let not man put asunder" (Mark 10:9)
58. Flat surfaces
59. "Thou shalt not take the name of the Lord thy God ___" (Exodus 20:7)
62. "When ye see a cloud rise out of the west, straightway ye say, There cometh a ___" (Luke 12:54)
63. Some hosp. workers
66. Billy Joel's instrument
67. "But of the tree of the knowledge of good and evil, thou shalt not ___" (Genesis 2:17)
68. "Amen!"
70. ACLU concerns (abbr)
71. How God led the Israelites out of Egypt (Exodus 13:21)
75. God said to her, "Two nations ___ in thy womb" (Genesis 25:23)
76. Shoe sections
77. On edge
78. "Is he the God of the Jews only? is he not also of the Gentiles? ___, of the Gentiles also" (Romans 3:29)
79. He was punished for hypocrisy and deceit (Acts 5:1–5)
80. Insulting look

Down

1. Dance it or dip it
2. Betel palm
3. Roman Empire invaders
4. Arsenal supply
5. Japanese farewell
6. Malt drink
7. ___ -Tzu, founder of Taoism
8. "... be thou an example of the believers, . . . in charity, in spirit, in faith, ___" (1 Timothy 4:12)
9. Cords to entangle animals
10. Toward the sheltered side
11. 1988 Hanks movie
12. "Then Samuel took the horn of oil, and ___ him in the midst of his bretheren" (1 Samuel 16:13)
13. "He that is without sin . . . , let him first cast a ___ at her" (John 8:7)
14. Grave risk
15. Actors Robert and Alan
20. "A time to ___, and a time to pluck up" (Ecclesiastes 3:2)
25. "Create in me a clean heart, ___" (Psalm 51:10)
28. Actress West
29. "But the ___ of all things is at hand" (1 Peter 4:7)
30. Classic TV's *Green* ___
31. Knife handle
32. Mouse-spotting cries
33. Michelangelo's post-Crucifixion sculpture

34. Ground breaker
35. "But one of the soldiers with a ___ pierced his side" (John 19:34)
36. Banjoist Scruggs
37. Charity
38. Zacchaeus said, "Behold, Lord, the ___ of my goods I give to the poor" (Luke 19:8)
39. Irish Rose lover
43. Van Dyke's role in *Diagnosis Murder*
44. Fizzling-out sound
45. Puppy bark
47. "___ bien!"
49. NE African nation
50. One of the 12 tribes of Israel
51. Hams it up
53. A fowl the Israelites are forbidden to eat (Leviticus 11:18)
54. ___-mo replay
55. Carpenter's tool
56. "___ by land..."
59. "___ not for the world, but for them which thou has given me" (John 17:9)
60. Saltpeter in Southampton
61. Rose bowls
62. Parlor
63. Male bee
64. Don't throw away
65. 52-Across, by another name
67. Actress Lanchester
69. Country singer Campbell
72. "... because there was no room for them in the ___" (Luke 2:7)
73. Actor Stephen
74. CIA forerunner (abbr)

1	2	3	4	5	■	6	7	8	9	10	11	12	■	13	14	15
16					■	17							■	18		
19					20								■	21		
22						■	■	23			■	24	25			
26			■	27		28	29			■	30					
■	■	■	31						■	32				■	■	■
■	■	33							34					35	36	37
38	39				■	■	■	40					■	41		
42				■	43	44	45	■	46			■	47			
48			■	49				50	■	■	■	51				
52			53						54	55	56				■	■
■	■	■	57				■	58						■	■	■
59	60	61				■	62						■	63	64	65
66					■	67			■	■	68		69			
70			■	71	72				73	74						
75			■	76							■	77				
78			■	79							■	80				

PARADISE LOST: THE MOVIE VERSION

Across

1. Kingdom
6. Give and take
10. Mardi ___
14. Open courtyards
15. Queen of this land visited Solomon (1 Kings 10:1–13)
16. Body eruption
17. Celeste Holm/Olivia de Havilland film (1948)
19. Had title to
21. Catch on
22. "If any man will ___ thee at the law, and take away thy coat, let him have thy cloak" (Matthew 5:40)
23. Race pace
25. Corduroy ridge
26. "The powers that be are ___ of God." (Romans 13:1)
29. "The ___ is not above his master" (Matthew 10:24)
31. Like some signature lines
33. Writer Eda Le ___
34. "I know thy works, and where thou dwellest, even where ___ seat is" (Revelation 2:13)
37. Yuletide drink
39. "I sink ___ mire, where there is no standing" (Psalm 69:2)
43. Molecule parts
44. Street market
46. *To Live and Die* ___ (1985 film)
47. Meter maid of song
48. Yukon, e.g. (abbr)
49. Vietnamese holiday
50. The Lord said unto the children of Israel, "Did ___ deliver you from the Egyptians" (Judges 10:11)
51. "For what shall it profit ___, if he shall gain the whole world, and lose his own soul?" (Mark 8:36)
52. Young cow
54. Wyoming range
55. Maintained
57. Proverb, suffix
58. Zealous
59. Jewish priest and scribe who led the reform of post-exile Jerusalem
61. "There went out a ___ from Caesar Augustus, that all the world should be taxed." (Luke 2:1)
63. Divine
67. Gathered bit by bit
71. Actor Alan
72. Wild attempt
74. Battleship letters
75. Govt. auditor
76. Big dipper
78. Bette Davis/Anne Baxter film (1950)
81. Playthings
82. Public uproars
83. Has merit
84. Feminine suffix
85. "The Lord ___ mark upon Cain" (Genesis 4:15)
86. "___ ye the Lord our God, and worship at his footstool; for he is holy." (Psalm 99:5)

Down

1. Dustin's *Midnight Cowboy* role
2. Early anesthetic
3. "And they smote him on the head with ___" (Mark 15:19)
4. Fleur-de-___
5. "In my Father's house are many ___" (John 14:2)
6. That ship
7. Sobbed
8. "Our soul is escaped as ___ out of the snare of the fowlers" (Psalm 124:7)
9. Jargon
10. 32-Down times twelve (abbr)
11. Jeff Chandler/Esther Williams film (1958)
12. "It's ___!" ("No problem!")
13. Beach find
15. Trapshooter's target
18. Polly, Rhody, and Em
20. Wallace of *E.T.*
24. Casual top
27. Stewart Granger/Jean Simmons film (1950)
28. Ancient Roman coins
30. Worm container
32. Egg-buyer's qty.
34. Abraham's wife
35. "To every thing there is a season, and ___ to every purpose under the heaven" (Ecclesiastes 3:1)

36. Out-and-out
38. Drop-leaf table feature
40. Short Internet message
41. Sir John of pop
42. Put on a coat
44. Honey maker
45. ___ Lingus
48. "And when they had plaited a crown of ___, they put it upon his head" (Matthew 27:29)
53. Fleeting fashion
54. "For where your ___ is, there will your heart be also." (Matthew 6:21)
56. Chinese philosopher Lao-___
58. "I marvel that ye ___ soon removed from him that called you into the grace" (Galatians 1:6)
60. "But ye shall destroy their ___, break their images, and cut down their groves" (Exodus 34:13)
62. Golf bag items
63. *2001* computer
64. Fill with joy
65. Extension
66. New Haven collegian
68. "___ Kick Out of You"
69. Orange variety
70. ". . . for whither thou ___, I will go" (Ruth 1:16)
73. "Hide thy face from my sins, and ___ out all mine iniquities." (Psalm 51:9)
77. Legal, suffix
79. One-time link
80. Put a strain on

1	2	3	4	5	■	■	6	7	8	9	■	10	11	12	13	■
14					■	15					■	16				■
17					18						■	19				20
21			■	22			■	23			24	■	25			
26			27				28	■	29			30				
■	■	■	31					32	■	33				■	■	■
34	35	36				■	37		38	■	39			40	41	42
43					■	44				45		■	46			
47				■	48			■	49			■	50			
51				■	52			53			■	54				
55				56		■	57			■	58					
■	■	■	59			60	■	61		62				■	■	■
63	64	65					66	■	67					68	69	70
71				■	72			73	■	74			■	75		
76				77	■	78			79				80			
■	81				■	82					■	83				
■	84				■	85				■	■	86				

Cross Swords

Across

1. Where Jesus found a Samaritan drawing water (John 4:7)
5. Emulated John's disciples (Mark 2:18)
11. Coffee shop order
16. Toward the sheltered side
17. Mexican food brand
18. Marveled aloud
19. He almost had a baby cut in two with a sword (1 Kings 3:25)
21. Links legend Sam
22. Dog on *Frasier*
23. Vs.
24. Longstreet's country (abbr)
26. Grandmother of Enos (Genesis 4:26)
27. Florida explorer
29. They draw a sword on poor people (Psalm 37:14)
32. Unashamedly unclothed, in Genesis 2:25
35. *Fear of Flying* author Jong
36. www addresses
39. Word on a French map
40. Colo. clock setting
41. "Look ___ hands!"
45. Name of 13 popes
46. Jethro, to Moses (Exodus 18:1)
48. Griller of wise men (Matthew 2:7)
49. He stood before Balaam with sword drawn (Numbers 22:31)
54. Singer Lou
55. Mistaken identity for Jesus (Mark 6:15)
56. NNW's opposite
57. Respected son of Adam (Genesis 4:4)
58. Frequent foe of Syria (abbr)
61. Informational programming (abbr)
62. Gad's job, under David (2 Samuel 24:11)
63. Vital vessel
65. '50s marionette name
67. They're like sword thrusts (Proverbs 12:18, NRSV)
71. Mount of Elijah's victory (1 Kings 18)
75. QB's misfire (abbr)
76. Opposite of SSW
77. "And there will ___ buried" (Ruth 1:17)
80. Anne Frank account
81. Fruit of the Spirit (Galatians 5:22)
83. He saw Saul fall on his sword (1 Samuel 31:4–5)
86. Princes could not find this in Daniel (Daniel 6:4)
87. Ceiling-hung art piece
88. Riviera resort
89. Speaks hoarsely
90. Marked with the king's ring (Esther 8:8)
91. Parts of a match

Down

1. Faced a new day
2. Say "nothin'," say
3. Happens at the banks of the Jordan
4. Angel units (Matthew 26:53)
5. Egg ___ yong
6. Guthrie with a guitar
7. Where to get off
8. Satan's job
9. Type of trip
10. Daughter of Herodias and others (Matthew 14:6)
11. Writings of Aaron's brother
12. Ends ball or bass
13. Turn it, when hit (Luke 6:29)
14. Chuck
15. Tacked on
20. Stiff bristle
25. Loretta of *M*A*S*H*
28. Giving the green light to
30. Haw's companion
31. Clothing source for John (Matthew 3:4)
33. Fashion mag
34. "It's the real ___!"
36. Part of UHF
37. Place for Noah after the wine
38. "Camelot" composer
42. Made the first Easter possible
43. Like Eric the Red
44. More off-the-wall
46. "___ and outs"
47. Word for lamentation
48. "___ got the whole world"
50. God of the Koran

51. Reacted like the disciples in Gethsemane (Matthew 26:56)
52. Brother of Michael Jackson
53. Utter chaos
58. Caananite chariot material
59. Desert signs of hope, for Isaiah (Isaiah 35:6)
60. "Far out!"
62. Naaman and others (2 Kings 5:1)
64. Title holders
66. Miami-___ County
67. Less green
68. The end of ___
69. Night rulers, in Genesis 1:16
70. *The Lion King* hero
72. Jesus' mother, to Jeanne d'Arc
73. Put up
74. Old strings
78. Leviticus sore (Leviticus 13:18)
79. ___ Stanley Gardner
82. Radar gun wielder
84. Future fish
85. "Take up thy ___" (Matthew 9:6)

THE MIRACLE WORKER

Across

1. Trepidation
5. "It is easier for a camel to go through the eye of a needle, than for ___ man to enter into the kingdom of God." (Mark 10:25)
10. Kind of clock
15. Legal memo words
16. Region west of Hong Kong
17. Breakfast food
19. With only five loaves and two fishes, Jesus . . . (John 6:1–13)
22. Tiny amount
23. Dry as a bone
24. Morales of *La Bamba*
25. "___; Blessed is he that cometh in the name of the Lord" (Mark 11:9)
28. Held the deed to
31. Hellenic H
32. The psalms, essentially
34. Append
36. "The trees of the Lord are full of ___" (Psalm 104:16)
39. In defiance of death, Jesus . . . (John 11:43–44)
44. Lyric poems
46. Officially recorded (abbr)
47. Site of Muhammad's tomb
48. Nuclear physicist Enrico
50. ". . . he leadeth me beside the ___ waters." (Psalm 23:2)
53. Competitor
54. T.S. and George
56. Pond duck
58. Flying start
59. During a raging tempest, Jesus . . . (John 6:18–19)
63. LBJ's successor (abbr)
64. Snap course
65. Total again
67. Dot-___ (Internet business)
70. ". . . immediately there met him out of the ___ a man with an unclean spirit" (Mark 5:2)
72. "And it came to pass at the end of two full years, that Pharaoh ___" (Genesis 41:1)
76. "For what shall it profit ___, if he shall gain the whole world, and lose his own soul?" (Mark 8:36)
78. Addressed the court
80. One of the Muses
81. At a wedding in Cana, Jesus . . . (John 2:1–11)
86. Irrational fear
87. One-on-one teacher
88. Actresses Balin and Claire
89. "I will praise the name of God with ___" (Psalm 69:30)
90. "But one of the soldiers with a ___ pierced his side" (John 19:34)
91. "As a bird that wandereth from her ___, so is a man that wandereth from his place." (Proverbs 27:8)

Down

1. "And the evening and the morning were the ___ day." (Genesis 1:23)
2. January in Juarez
3. Regions
4. Train station employee
5. Qty.
6. Crowd cry
7. Bumps off
8. Small role for a big star
9. "And when the sixth ___ come, there was darkness over the whole land" (Mark 15:33)
10. ". . . the ___ of violence is in their hands." (Isaiah 59:6)
11. Island chain
12. Johnson of *Laugh-In*
13. Employ again
14. Upset with
18. Darth's daughter
20. Monterrey mister
21. Ivan of tennis
26. "The Lord is ___ upon all the heathen" (Obadiah 1:15)
27. Female friends of François
29. Dutch treat
30. Earth mover, for short
33. Army NCO (abbr)
35. Gymnast Comaneci
36. "Never in the field of human conflict was so much owed by so many to ___." (Winston Churchill)
37. Writer St. Johns
38. "We gat our bread with the ___ of our lives because of the sword of the wilderness." (Lamentations 5:9)

40. Writer Wharton
41. "And a ___ went out of Eden to water the garden" (Genesis 2:10)
42. Render defenseless
43. Parlor
45. "For my days are consumed like ___" (Psalm 102:3)
49. Where ___ (trendy place)
51. Lascivious look
52. Used a surgical light
55. Just okay
57. Shakespearean king
60. Mythic nature goddess
61. Stone slabs, upon which God inscribed the Ten Commandments
62. Doe follower, in song
66. *Origin of Species* author
67. "And the angel of God, which went before the ___ of Israel" (Exodus 14:19)
68. Nebraska city
69. Dangerous sharks
71. Clinch, as a victory
73. Pine Tree state
74. Old lab burners
75. "For thou art great, and ___ wondrous things" (Psalm 86:10)
77. Mountain from which Moses last views Canaan before he dies
79. Palm tree fruit
82. "... go, and ___ no more." (John 8:11)
83. "You're it!" game
84. Burnt-crisp link
85. "O Lord, why hast thou made us to ___ from thy ways?" (Isaiah 63:17)

1	2	3	4	■	5	6	7	8	9	■	10	11	12	13	14	■
15				■	16					■	17					18
19				20						21						
22					■	■	23				■	■	24			
25					26	27	■	28			29	30	■	31		
■	■	■	32				33	■	34				35	■	■	■
36	37	38	■	39				40						41	42	43
44			45	■	46				■	■	47					
48				49	■	50			51	52	■	53				
54					55	■	■	56			57	■	58			
59						60	61					62	■	63		
■	■	■	64					■	65				66	■	■	■
67	68	69	■	70				71	■	72				73	74	75
76			77	■	■	78			79	■	■	80				
81				82	83					84	85					
86						■	87					■	88			
■	89					■	90					■	91			

SERVICE STATIONS

Across

1. Svelte
5. Jezebel's deity (1 Kings 16:31)
9. Demolish
14. A piece of music
15. "Follow me, ___ will make you fishers of men." (Matthew 4:19)
16. Home of Bedouin descendants of Ishmael
18. Beany's puppet sidekick of old TV
19. Major golf tournaments
20. "He heard the words of ___ sons, saying, Jacob hath taken away all that was our father's" (Genesis 31:1)
21. Sanctuary where Jesus drove out the money changers
24. Summers on the Riviera
25. Utah city
26. Some art works
27. "And Ruth said, ___ me not to leave thee" (Ruth 1:16)
29. Grinch creator
31. Tormentor of Job (Job 2:7)
32. Tree from which Absalom hung
35. Shade tree
36. Long, long time
37. Religious teacher (John 3:2)
41. Laboratory containers
43. ". . . and him that cometh to me I will ___ wise cast out." (John 6:37)
44. Random House cofounder Bennett
45. Bar members (abbr)
46. Expand
47. Grip aid
48. Hoffman's ___ *Man*
49. Idle
50. "___ not the Spirit." (1 Thessalonians 5:19)
51. Best of the crop
53. Deli order (abbr)
54. Astronaut Grissom
55. Wide shoe size
56. "___ our refuge and strength, a very present help in trouble." (Psalm 46:1)
58. Whose boat survived the flood?
60. Third king of ancient Israel
63. Remove, as a hat
64. Mandlikova of tennis
68. TV show (abbr)
69. Original ziggurat (Genesis 11:1–9)
72. "The glory of the Lord shall ___ for ever" (Psalm 104:31)
74. Ancestor of Abraham (Genesis 11:17–26)
75. "And the Holy Ghost descended in a bodily shape like ___ upon him" (Luke 3:22)
76. Mark with a fold
77. Formerly
78. Is a sign of
79. Trial balloons
80. A trodden way
81. Fancy pitcher

Down

1. Operate the helm
2. "For a bishop must be blameless, . . . not given to filthy ___" (Titus 1:7)
3. Dialect features
4. Pinochle play
5. "One Lord, one faith, one ___" (Ephesians 4:5)
6. Michael and Gabriel
7. "Dilbert" cartoonist Scott
8. Speak like Sylvester
9. Gold coin during Jesus' day
10. "Though I speak with the tongues of men and of angels, and have not charity, I am become as sounding brass, ___ tinkling cymbal." (1 Corinthians 13:1)
11. Portable sanctuary of the wandering Israelites (Numbers 1:51)
12. Die down
13. Top of a form, perhaps
14. Back talk
17. DA's aide (abbr)
22. "He that winneth ___ is wise." (Proverbs 11:30)
23. Use for support
28. Roofing material
30. Mouse-spotting cries
31. "Whosoever shall confess that Jesus is the ___ God, God dwelleth in him, and he in God." (1 John 4:15)
32. Joan ___ (French saint)
33. Sacrifice site
34. *Today* host Couric

36. Conclude by
38. Designer Geoffrey
39. Prop up
40. "___ salt have lost his savour, wherewith shall it be salted?" (Matthew 5:13)
42. Local houses of worship and instruction (Matthew 4:23)
43. Heroes
46. White rabbit, e.g.
47. Son of Ham and ancestor of many nations (Genesis 10:6)
50. Guzzle down
52. Pop's partner
54. "___ of the ark, thou, and thy wife, and thy sons" (Genesis 8:16)
57. Grandparents, sometimes
58. "The dove found ___ for the sole of her foot, and she returned unto him into the ark" (Genesis 8:9)
59. Follow secretly
60. Hotfooted it
61. "What thinkest thou? Is it lawful to give tribute unto Caesar, ___?" (Matthew 22:17)
62. Inn
63. Winger of *An Officer and a Gentleman*
65. Temporary stay
66. "And whosoever liveth and believeth in me shall ___ die." (John 11:26)
67. Malt beverages
70. Sob
71. Baseball's Ruth
73. Spill the beans

■	1	2	3	4	■	5	6	7	8	■	9	10	11	12	13	■
14					■	15				■	16					17
18					■	19				■	20					
21					22					23		■	24			
25				■	26				■	27		28				
■	■	■	29	30				■	31					■	■	■
32	33	34	■	35			■	36			■	37		38	39	40
41		42				■	43				■	■	44			
45					■	46					■	47				
48				■	■	49				■	50					
51				52	■	53			■	54			■	55		
■	■	■	56		57			■	58				59	■	■	■
60	61	62					■	63				■	64	65	66	67
68				■	69	70						71				
72				73		■	74				■	75				
76						■	77				■	78				
■	79					■	80				■	81				■

When There's a Will

Across

1. Feudal lord's lands
6. "Do we ___ again to commend ourselves?" (2 Corinthians 3:1)
11. Ship parts made of Lebanon cedars (Ezekiel 27:5)
16. "But they can't find ___ for the common cold!"
17. "He hath turned ___ my ways" (Lamentations 3:11)
18. Arctic abode
19. Toil
20. Adam gave these to the animals (Genesis 2:20)
21. What God is in Judah (Psalm 76:1)
22. Too short to see Jesus, Zacchaeus ___ (Luke 19:4)
25. "The Rebels" school, familiarly
26. What Moses did to the Egyptian (Exodus 2:12)
27. "Pow!"
31. "___ boy!"
33. Spanish married ladies (abbr)
35. U.N. workers' grp.
36. On a par, in Paris
40. Head circle often found in religious art
42. Strands via wintry weather
44. Fountain orders
46. Computer network terminal
48. Speakers' platforms
49. To be cured by Jesus despite the crowds, the woman simply ___ (Luke 8:44)
52. She played *Annie* in 1982
53. Car
54. Shopping binge
55. Claws
57. Darius, for one (Daniel 9:1)
59. Strategic WWI river
60. Winter hrs. in Boston
61. Last word in all four Gospels
63. Young newts
65. Fr. holy women
67. Militarily fit
69. Plastic used for film
74. With conventional entry unavailable, a palsied man's friends lowered him ___ (Mark 2:4)
77. Mudville's disappointing batter
80. Bathsheba's first husband (2 Samuel 11:3)
81. More desperate
82. What God wanted animals to do abundantly (Genesis 8:17)
83. *Good Times* star, in 1970s TV
84. "___ nous" ("Just between us")
85. Like week-old bread
86. Scornful look
87. Update the arsenal

Down

1. Actress Edie of *The Sopranos*
2. "Henceforth ___ you not servants" (John 15:15)
3. Jazz artist Blake
4. German-born psychoanalyst Erich
5. Where Belgrade is
6. Concert platform
7. Twin who was "a cunning hunter" (Genesis 25:27)
8. Walks with a hobble
9. Paragons
10. Avian homemakers
11. Wallace of *60 Minutes*
12. Nixon's first vice president
13. ___-mo (instant replay speed)
14. Remove, as an illegally parked car
15. James, to Zebedee (Matthew 4:21)
23. Bk. after Neh.
24. Kigali's land
28. They greet the stage villian
29. Property receiver, in court
30. Hobgoblin
32. Oahu greeting
34. Flies like an eagle
36. Will concerns
37. Maudlin to the max
38. Flatter excessively
39. Ice skater, before skating
41. Loathing
43. Popeye's hamburger-loving pal

45. "___ Woman" (Beatles' tune)
47. Cosmetic titan Lauder
50. Fill with love
51. Baptismal sponsor
56. Singers (Brit var)
58. Draw with acid
62. Nerve cell
64. Farmer, at times
66. Durable alloy
68. Nimble
70. Threefold
71. Important heart trunk
72. ". . . and their lies caused them ___" (Amos 2:4)
73. Stephanie Zimbalist's dad
75. Jekyll's vicious side
76. Healthy
77. Network with an eye logo (abbr)
78. "Where ___ thou?" (God's question to Adam, Genesis 3:9)
79. Through Moses, the Lord parted one (Exodus 14:21)

1	2	3	4	5	■	6	7	8	9	10	■	11	12	13	14	15
16					■	17					■	18				
19					■	20					■	21				
22					23						24			■	■	■
25							■	26				■	27	28	29	30
■	■	■	■	31			32	■	33			34	■	35		
36	37	38	39	■	40			41	■	42			43			
44				45	■	46			47	■	48					
49					50					51						
52						■	53				■	54				
55						56	■	57			58	■	59			
60			■	61			62	■	63			64	■	■	■	■
65			66	■	67			68	■	69			70	71	72	73
■	■	■	74	75					76							
77	78	79			■	80					■	81				
82					■	83					■	84				
85					■	86					■	87				

PASSION WEEK

Across

1. Sailor's bed
6. The Prodigal Son, for one (Luke 15:11–32)
13. Shea Stadium player
16. Social critic Cleveland
17. Firewood support
18. Pub selection
19. Garden betrayer (Matthew 26:46–49)
21. "Sprechen ___ Deutsch?"
22. Basketball stats
23. Susan of *Five Easy Pieces*
25. His wife became a pillar of salt (Genesis 19:23–26)
26. Org.
29. "And if ___ before I wake . . ." (child's prayer)
30. Lose firmness
33. He condemned Jesus to be crucified (Matthew 27:11–26)
37. Turkish chiefs
39. Flow slowly
40. Heart chart (abbr)
41. Inauguration of Holy Communion (Matthew 26:20–30)
44. Boot camp bosses
48. Pacify
49. City on Paul's second missionary journey (Acts 18:1)
50. "Neither shalt thou ___ thy neighbour's wife" (Deuteronomy 5:21)
51. Site of Jesus' betrayal (Matthew 26:36–46)
54. A Bobbsey twin
55. Part of a plot
56. Run through
57. Symbol of Jesus' mockery (Matthew 27:29)
63. Retirees' org.
64. Arizona border city
65. ". . . unto us ___ is given" (Isaiah 9:6)
66. Merchandise bars (abbr)
68. Pretend
71. Fires up
75. Stimpy's toon pal
76. He bore Jesus' cross to Calvary (Matthew 27:32)
80. Mentalist Geller
81. Ogle
82. Sir John of pop
83. Radiator sound
84. Chicken or fish tidbits
85. Friars Club event

Down

1. Mexican peninsula
2. Ostrich cousins
3. Shepherd's staffs
4. Follow the leader
5. Reed used to lift the vinegar-filled sponge to Jesus' lips (John 19:29)
6. "And it came to ___ in those days . . ." (Luke 2:1)
7. Mandela's org.
8. Nutrition letters
9. Tire filler
10. Actor Dennehy and director DePalma
11. Crazy bird
12. Tolkien creatures
13. Ancient Israeli fortress
14. Draw forth
15. Tiny titter
20. "I will cause ___ rain upon the earth forty days and forty nights" (Genesis 7:4)
24. Visitors to a sacred shrine
26. Perched on
27. Petite or jumbo
28. Plaintiff
30. Caesar, for one
31. Slack-jawed
32. Sounds of surprise
34. Slangy refusal
35. Mexican currency
36. Words of empathy
38. Popular piano
42. It's a wrap
43. "___ Hooks" (words on a shipping crate)
45. Bitty biters
46. Italian volcano (poss)
47. Queen of this land visited Solomon (1 Kings 10:1–13)
49. *Moonstruck* actress
51. Hoods' weapons
52. Talk back

53. Jeff Bridges sci-fi flick (1982)
57. Paul's first mission (Acts 13:4–12)
58. Pharoahs and kings
59. Muscat residents
60. *Jake and the* ___ (William Conrad TV drama)
61. ___ Dimittis (Simeon's song of thanks, Luke 2:29–32)
62. More agile
67. Monte ___
69. Mgr.'s helper
70. Refer to
71. Aquatic newts
72. "___ life!"
73. Nephew of Cain (Genesis 4:25–26)
74. "He that believeth on me, believeth not on me, but on him that ___ me." (John 12:44)
77. Former California fort
78. Family tree word
79. Dinghy propeller

1	2	3	4	5	■	6	7	8	9	10	11	12	■	13	14	15
16					■	17							■	18		
19					20								■	21		
22							■	■	■	23			24			
■	■	■	25			■	26	27	28		■	■	29			
30	31	32	■	33		34					35	36				
37			38	■	■	39				■	40			■	■	■
41				42	43					■	44			45	46	47
48							■	■	■	49						
50						■	51	52	53							
■	■	■	54			■	55				■	■	56			
57	58	59				60					61	62	■	63		
64				■	■	65				■	66		67	■	■	■
68				69	70		■	■	■	71				72	73	74
75			■	76			77	78	79							
80			■	81							■	82				
83			■	84							■	85				

THE RAINMAKER

Across

1. Walker coin
5. Dressed like a judge
10. Newman's *Absence of* ___
16. "And at the ninth hour Jesus cried with a loud voice, saying Eloi, ___, lama sabachthani?" (Mark 15:34)
17. Burn ___ in one's pocket
18. "All these are the twelve ___ of Israel" (Genesis 49:28)
19. "And he ___ upon a cherub, and did fly" (2 Samuel 22:11)
20. Symbolism of the rainbow (Genesis 9:12–15)
22. God's command to Noah (Genesis 6:14)
24. Art Deco designer
25. Twosome
26. Damascus resident
29. ___ *Boot*
32. *Cleopatra,* for one
35. Visual lang.
36. "___, and pay unto the Lord your God" (Psalm 76:11)
39. Tracy and Hepburn's ___ *Rib*
41. Arias
44. Pacific atoll
46. Mountain from which Moses last views Canaan before he dies
47. "For ___ dwelleth all the fulness of the Godhead bodily." (Colossians 2:9)
48. *Wuthering Heights* actress
49. Noah's token of thanksgiving for being spared (Genesis 8:20)
52. Mercury or Saturn
54. Showed again
55. "I did cast them out as the ___ in the streets." (Psalm 18:42)
58. Contend
59. "___ bien!"
60. Reluctant prophet to Ninevah
61. Mark of penitence (Daniel 9:3)
62. Tiny creature
64. Architect Saarinen
66. "And Moses sent them to ___ out the land of Canaan" (Numbers 13:17)
67. Bit players
70. "In and ___"
72. Author Haley
75. Part of Nehemiah's booth (Nehemiah 8:15)
81. Birds sent by Noah to seek dry land (Genesis 8:7–8)
84. Scarce
85. Egyptian god of the underworld
86. Shrine
87. Land inhabited by the descendants of Esau (Genesis 32:3)
88. Nile formations
89. "___ thou how faith wrought with his works, and by works was faith made perfect?" (James 2:22)
90. Dupes

Down

1. Alpert of the Tijuana Brass
2. Baseball family name
3. City near Sacramento
4. "Consider the lilies of the ___, how they grow" (Matthew 6:28)
5. Convertible, informally
6. Computer error
7. Be a sign of
8. Lanchester and Maxwell
9. Condemn openly
10. Video network
11. Live and breathe
12. Made of flax
13. Irish saint
14. Penny
15. Noble Italian family
21. Cajun vegetable
23. Fees
27. "For unto us a child ___, unto us a son is given" (Isaiah 9:6)
28. Cover story
29. One of the 12 sons of Jacob (Genesis 30:6)
30. Citrus drink
31. Day of rest
33. Fails to be
34. Partner in crime
36. Chaste people
37. Lennon's love
38. Take the gold
40. Sermon on the ___ (Matthew 5—7)
42. Career soldier
43. Hit song from the rock opera *Tommy*
45. Japanese fencing

47. Purpose
50. Take five
51. Freedom from care
52. Alley org.
53. Vegas opener
56. Music store section
57. "And he said to the woman, ___ faith hath saved thee; go in peace." (Luke 7:50)
60. Soup du ___
63. 1982 cyberflick
65. Poet Frost
67. Apply, as pressure
68. Actors Robert and Alan
69. Move like a crab
71. "But while men slept, his enemy came and sowed ___ among the wheat, and went his way." (Matthew 13:25)
72. "And there shall come forth ___ out of the stem of Jesse, and a Branch shall grow out of his roots" (Isaiah 11:1)
73. Emit coherent light
74. Welles's *Touch of* ___
76. Cast a ballot
77. Bartok and Gabor
78. Nothing, to Zapata
79. Riding whip
80. Clothes lines
82. Actress Peeples
83. "And Jesus, when he had found a young ___, sat thereon" (John 12:14)

1	2	3	4	■	5	6	7	8	9	■	10	11	12	13	14	15
16				■	17					■	18					
19				■	20					21						
22				23							■	■	24			
■	■	■	25			■	■	26			27	28		■	■	■
29	30	31	■	32		33	34	■	■	35			■	36	37	38
39			40		■	41		42	43	■	44		45			
46				■	47					■	48					
■	■	49		50						51					■	■
52	53					■	54					■	55		56	57
58						■	59				■	60				
61			■	62		63	■	■	64		65		■	66		
■	■	■	67				68	69	■	■	70		71	■	■	■
72	73	74		■	■	75			76	77				78	79	80
81				82	83							■	84			
85						■	86					■	87			
88						■	89					■	90			

Run for Your Lives

Across

1. Display
5. Consort of Zeus
9. Middles
15. French Sudan, today
16. Acid in proteins
18. Words of agreement
19. " . . . when saw we thee sick, ___ prison . . . ?" (Matthew 25:39)
20. Vintage photograph shade
21. Suzanne of *Three's Company*
22. "David, flee from the palace!"
25. *Xanadu* rock grp.
26. Seine waters
27. Has ___ with (is connected to)
29. Sunday singer
33. Superficial coverings
36. Bumpkin
37. With 55-Across, "Jesus, Mary, and Joseph, exit to Egypt!"
39. Gold-coated
40. Without face value, as stock
42. *Happy Days* malt shop owner
43. Iron lever
45. Obstinate
50. Painter's plaster
51. TV's talking horse
55. See 37-Across
57. Most unsure
59. Throw away
60. Sins
61. Put cargo away
62. Carve in stone
65. Vietnamese holiday
66. "Moses, make off for Midian!"
72. Actress Bloom
74. Make ___ (strike it rich)
75. " . . . are ye angry ___ because . . . ?" (John 7:23)
76. "The Conference of Champions," commonly
77. Mr. Arafat
78. What they will do upon the Lord (Micah 3:11)
79. Fast
80. Belgian river
81. Lith. and Ukr., formerly

Down

1. Urban haze
2. Mata ___
3. Popeye's gal
4. Sommelier's offering
5. ___ point (makes sense)
6. Flightless bird (var)
7. "Believe It or Not" creator
8. Writer Loos
9. "If thy father at all ___ me, then say. . ." (1 Samuel 20:6)
10. Asa's mother, for one (1 Kings 15:13)
11. What God gave humans over the creatures he created (Genesis 1:26)
12. Fill, as another's shoes
13. Craggy hill
14. "Mayday!"
17. Where Pearl Harbor is
23. "And the famine was ___ in the land." (Genesis 43:1)
24. Lab proj.
28. Jael's weapon (Judges 4:21)
29. Fee (abbr)
30. "Bali ___"
31. Takes out of the game
32. Smell
34. Way, way out there
35. Leaving Logan (abbr)
37. Hemmed and ___
38. Eyes, poetically
41. Walt Kelly's possum
44. "We grope ___ we had no eyes . . ." (Isaiah 59:10)
45. Made in a factory (abbr)
46. *Exodus* author
47. Was shamed
48. Rude
49. Rained briefly
51. Vitamins and ___

52. Iterates
53. U-turn from WNW
54. Certain football positions (abbr)
56. Coral formation
58. Greek cheese
60. "Excuse me, waitress?"
63. Cafeteria item
64. HMO requirement, often
67. Start of a choosing rhyme
68. Ballet bend
69. Hauss mister
70. Esau's grandson (Genesis 36:15)
71. Coop group
72. A hertz equals one (abbr)
73. The lot is cast into this, according to Proverbs 16:33

He Is Risen!

Across

1. Andre of tennis
7. "For this is my blood of the new testament, which is shed for many for the remission ___." (Matthew 26:28)
13. Bro's sib
16. Director Bergman
17. Snookums
18. NY clock setting
19. First person to see the risen Savior (Mark 16:9)
21. Future fish
22. Swabbies
23. ___ buco (veal dish)
24. *Amistad* passenger
26. Words of denial
28. Fed
31. German automaker
32. Have in mind
34. Burial place of Jesus (John 19:41–42)
36. Screw-cutting tool
37. "Not ___ now ye that are men, and serve the Lord" (Exodus 10:11)
39. Salad-dressing cheese
40. "Well, Did You ___?" (Cole Porter tune)
42. Semi-convertible car roofs
45. "Love ___ you need" (Beatles refrain)
49. Provider of Jesus' burial place (Matthew 27:57–60 NIV)
53. Rose oil
54. Actor Joe of *Hill Street Blues*
55. "Moses and Aaron went in unto Pharaoh, and they did ___ the Lord had commanded" (Exodus 7:10)
56. Nullify
59. Chanted
61. Fizzling sound
62. Occasion of Jesus' return to heaven (Luke 24:50–51)
67. Adam Smith's ___ *of Nations*
69. "You're putting ___!"
70. Actress Lange
71. Model Macpherson
72. Get up!
74. Montreal baseball player
76. "___ Rhythm"
79. Buddhist sect
80. Site of Jesus' farewell to his apostles (Acts 1:12 NIV)
85. Opposite of WSW
86. Specks in the ocean
87. Lubricates again
88. Family man
89. On ___ (punctual)
90. "___ to Caesar the things that are Caesar's, and to God the things that are God's." (Mark 12:17)

Down

1. Align the crosshairs
2. Puny pest
3. Taj Mahal site
4. One of the seven churches in the Book of Revelation
5. "And ___ wife wept before him, and said, Thou dost but hate me" (Judges 14:16)
6. A captain in David's army (1 Chronicles 27:9)
7. Vegas numbers
8. Passover, e.g. (John 2:23)
9. She was present at Jesus' crucifixion (Mark 15:40)
10. Bad temper
11. Diarist Anaïs
12. Gets the picture
13. An angel, attendant to God (Isaiah 6:2 NIV)
14. "And, behold, Amariah the chief priest ___ you in all matters of the Lord" (2 Chronicles 19:11)
15. Brosnan TV role
20. "The Lord said unto Satan, Whence comest thou? Then Satan answered the Lord, and said, From ___ and fro in the earth" (Job 1:7)
25. Eighth plague of Egypt (Exodus 10:12–15)
27. "___ and nail"
29. LAPD alert
30. No one, in Nice
32. Point
33. Opposite of most
35. *Star Wars* princess
36. ___ vu
38. Cartoon punch reactions
41. Skies

43. Baby food
44. Ladies of Spain (abbr)
46. What Gaius was to Paul (Romans 16:23)
47. Terrier tether
48. Glasgow girl
50. Pt. of speech
51. "Let all the earth fear the Lord: let all the inhabitants of the world stand ___ him." (Psalm 33:8)
52. Nickel alloy
57. "Somewhat" suffix
58. It gave, in Granada
60. Land where Jesus spent most of his life
62. "And he went up unto them into the ship; and the wind ceased: and they were sore ___ . . ." (Mark 6:51)
63. Sister of Venus
64. Invented, linguistically
65. Not shut
66. "And if his father have no brethren, then ye shall give his inheritance unto his kinsman that is ___ him of his family" (Numbers 27:11)
68. Many
73. Give off
75. Washington paper
77. *Metamorphoses* poet
78. The "T" in TV
81. Site of OSU campus
82. Little ending
83. Bobby of hockey
84. Cold War adversary (abbr)

THE STONES' GREATEST HITS

Across

1. Take it up and follow Jesus (Mark 10:21)
6. Baby in the bulrushes (Exodus 2:3, 10)
11. Seth's father, and others (Genesis 4:25)
16. Some are "out to ___"
17. "You're ___ talk"
18. Bother persistently
19. Host at a roast
20. Didn't stop
21. "___ is the kingdom" (Matthew 6:13)
22. Temple part made of costly stones (1 Kings 5:17)
24. Jacob used a stone for this (Genesis 28:18)
25. Zacchaeus climbed one (Luke 19:2–4)
26. Roseanne, once
27. To boot
28. Accident victims go there
29. Iranian currency
31. Get this before making war (Proverbs 20:18)
34. Bridges of *Airplane!*
37. Puts to work
38. Owned by Shem's brother (Genesis 9:18)
41. Name of God (Exodus 3:14)
42. Make, as a CD
45. "I knew it!"
47. Reformer Jacob
49. Samuel gave this name to a stone (1 Samuel 7:12)
51. Jacob and Laban piled up stones as a sign of this (Genesis 31:44–47)
53. NASA cancellation
54. Halogen suffix
55. Had an obligation
56. Gave de ___, French river
57. Sitarist Shankar
59. Night ender
61. "The third day he shall rise ___." (Mark 10:34)
63. Actress Lansbury
65. Tibetan monk
67. FICA funds it
70. Way out
71. Temple curtain
73. Similar to
77. Peter's name, which means "rock" (John 1:42)
79. A stone sealed this prison for Daniel (Daniel 6:16–17)
81. For the birds
82. Well-spoken brother of Moses (Exodus 4:14)
83. Female singing voices
84. Paul, among the apostles, per Paul (1 Corinthians 15:9)
85. Shaft of arrow
86. Simeon asked to depart in this (Luke 2:29)
87. Father-in-law of Caiaphas (John 18:13)
88. Piano part
89. Office furniture

Down

1. Hoof characteristic (Deuteronomy 14:6)
2. Unfounded story
3. When expected
4. Sights to enjoy
5. Spilled, as Christ's blood (Luke 22:20)
6. Like flesh
7. Where the elated walk
8. Ladies of Spain
9. Thames town
10. James, to Zebedee (Luke 5:10)
11. Where Paul withstood Peter (Galatians 2:11)
12. Writer Roald
13. Light-footed
14. Where the Lord lives
15. Crockpot concoctions
23. Attorneys' org.
24. Luau dish
27. *60 Minutes,* for one
30. "___ delighted!"
32. Church office
33. Pull down
34. Legal claim
35. Do this for six days (Exodus 20:9 NRSV)
36. Symbol of Christ as the end (Revelation 21:6)
37. Imaginary
39. Nevada valley

40. Where 6-Across took two tablets (Exodus 19:20; 32:15)
43. Israeli submachine gun
44. Do it to Caesar (Mark 12:17)
46. Greeting to Maria
48. Leave speechless
50. Kind of star
52. Holland export
58. The disciples tried to keep them from Jesus (Luke 18:15)
60. Ran hot and cold
62. Sea where Jesus recruited (Matthew 4:18)
64. Auto fuel
65. Actor Barrymore
66. Sitcom alien
67. Milan's La ___ opera house
68. The number of times Peter would forgive (Matthew 18:21)
69. For the bees
72. ___ Gay
74. Greek letter, pl.
75. What Jesus does at the door (Revelation 3:20)
76. Road curves
78. ___ cow (flips out)
79. Go out with
80. Sgt. Friday's force (abbr)
82. Nile biter

1	2	3	4	5	■	6	7	8	9	10	■	11	12	13	14	15
16					■	17					■	18				
19					■	20					■	21				
22					23					■	24					
25				■	26				■	27			■	28		
■	■	■	29	30			■	31	32				33	■	■	■
34	35	36			■	■	37				■	38		39	40	■
41			■	42	43	44		■	45		46	■	47			48
49			50					■	51			52				
53				■	54			■	55				■	56		
■	57			58	■	59		60		■	■	61	62			
■	■	■	63		64				■	65	66			■	■	■
67	68	69	■	70			■	71	72			■	73	74	75	76
77			78			■	79					80				
81					■	82					■	83				
84					■	85					■	86				
87					■	88					■	89				

Render unto Caesar

Across

1. "... heaven, where neither moth nor rust ___ corrupt" (Matthew 6:20)
5. Like a leprechaun
10. Jesus spoke of a generation of these (Matthew 12:34)
16. Memo starter
17. Still small sound (1 Kings 19:12)
18. Proverbs, e.g.
19. Mark of King Ahasuerus's ring (Esther 8:8)
20. Set up financially
21. Light at 1-Down
22. Sacred wafer
25. Get-go
26. Exactly as printed
27. Become spoiled
31. Inclination
35. CPR giver
37. College Web address suffix
38. Little bites
41. Hurling stats
43. What to do with 52-Across
46. Article in Acapulco
47. Absalom stole them from Israel's men (2 Samuel 15:6)
49. Hidden
50. "Ditto"
52. Dish
54. Papal crown
55. Prickly plants
57. Israelites in Egypt
59. Simon Peter let it into the sea (Luke 5:4)
60. Forever
62. Kristofferson of *A Star Is Born*
63. Jekyll's alter ego
64. ___ Tin Tin
65. Give a name to
67. Martha Finley's Dinsmore
69. Stuffed to the gills
72. Hurrah
74. Taste with pleasure
78. Internal ___
83. Hand-washing governor (Matthew 27:24)
86. Tongue is like (Jeremiah 9:8)
87. Thames college
88. Place for prayer (Luke 12:3)
89. Make a joyful one unto God (Psalm 66:1)
90. It's hallowed, in the Lord's Prayer (Matthew 6:9)
91. Seamstresses
92. High priest, with Caiaphas (Luke 3:2)
93. Killed

Down

1. '70s hot spot
2. "That we may sit, ___ thy right hand" (Mark 10:37)
3. Coal haulers
4. Israelite military protection (Jeremiah 46:4)
5. "... death, ___ the death of the cross" (Philippians 2:8)
6. Actress Anderson
7. Pet name
8. Images to click on
9. Beginner
10. Bud holder
11. Dog collar attachment
12. Don of game shows
13. Self-esteem
14. Dixie soldier, short
15. NNW's opposite
23. Hagen of Hollywood
24. Law grp. north of the border
28. Home of Lazarus (John 11:1)
29. Stuck
30. For Sarah it came late in life
32. Bishopric seat
33. Mouth, in slang
34. Court figures
36. Pencil-game word
38. Book that tells of Balaam
39. At rest
40. Like those who wait for the Lord (2 Thessalonians 3:5)
42. Ear-holder, in Joseph's dream (Genesis 41:22)
44. Admission exams (abbr)
45. Bio. or chem.
47. Weapon used to blast Joshua's enemies (Joshua 6:5)
48. Fixed look
51. Opposite of 'neath
53. Wicked

56. Singing the blues
58. Winding curve
61. Angler's equipment
63. They declare the glory of God (Psalm 19:1)
66. Cereal topper, often
68. Jacob's God-given name (Genesis 32:28, abbr)
70. Tape deck button
71. Discourage
73. One of the Great Lakes
75. Critically important
76. "___ all ye faithful"
77. Continue a subscription
79. Docs for doggies, short
80. *Happy Days* actress Moran
81. HR slugger Sammy
82. Members of the flock
83. Philatelic items (abbr)
84. Capable of, suffix
85. "Every... hill shall be made ___" (Isaiah 40:4)

1	2	3	4	■	5	6	7	8	9	■	10	11	12	13	14	15
16				■	17					■	18					
19				■	20					■	21					
22				23						24				■	■	■
25					■	■	■	26			■	27		28	29	30
■	■	■	31		32	33	34	■	35		36	■	■	37		
38	39	40		■	41			42	■	43		44	45			
46			■	47					48	■	49					
50			51		■	52				53	■	54				
55					56	■	57				58		■	59		
60						61	■	62				■	63			
64			■	■	65		66	■	67			68		■	■	■
69			70	71	■	72		73	■	■	■	74		75	76	77
■	■	■	78		79				80	81	82					
83	84	85				■	86					■	87			
88						■	89					■	90			
91						■	92					■	93			

CIRCUIT RIDERS

Across

1. Job hunter (Job 1:12)
6. Dan, for example (Exodus 31:6)
11. Teatime treat
16. Garlic bulb
17. Makes tolerable
18. Be not conformed to this (Romans 12:2)
19. First name in talk
20. Dazzling success
21. Map legend, usually
22. Start of a riddle about circuit riders
25. Word of derision in Psalm 35:21
26. Antonio in *Evita*
27. Marilyn's ___ *Like It Hot*
28. Team cheer
30. Records (abbr)
33. Noted shoe collector
37. Chiding sound
40. Novelist Harper
42. Hotel posting
44. Aardvark's tidbit
45. More of the riddle
48. Prepare to pray
50. He did the Lord's work
51. Accepted eagerly
53. Trader for costly pottage (Genesis 25:32–33)
54. Tire track
56. End of the riddle
58. Ecol. watchdog
59. Zellweger of *Chicago*
61. Work on clothes
62. Rd. or hwy.
63. He stayed off the lions' menu
65. Sault ___ Marie
67. Deborah Kerr's ___ *and Sympathy*
69. Diner order, with "the"
71. Recruiting org.
73. Code-cracking org.
76. Answer to the riddle
82. Bright stars
83. Beach at Normandy
84. "That's it!"
85. Elijah, in a chariot of fire (2 Kings 2:11)
86. In ciphertext
87. Don't provoke your children to this (Colossians 3:21)
88. Takes it easy
89. Gray with age
90. Broke the eighth commandment (Exodus 20:15)

Down

1. One with a flat bottom
2. Omega counterpart (Revelation 1:8)
3. Numbers is one of five holy books
4. Krishna
5. *M*A*S*H* soft drink
6. Comb projections
7. Leah's sister (Genesis 29:16)
8. Cruise stop
9. Tuckered out
10. Senator Kefauver
11. Snorkeler's need
12. Compare opinions
13. Roughly
14. Met or Card
15. D.C. summer hrs.
23. 1961 Best Actor Maximilian
24. Paul's residence, in Acts 28
29. Will Smith title role
31. Major or minor
32. ___ Domingo
34. Render unto him what's his (Mark 12:17)
35. Like a short play
36. Holy writer and physician
37. "Ye have ___ that the Lord is gracious" (1 Peter 2:3)
38. Tenzing Norgay, for one
39. Seoul man or woman
41. Keep an ___ him
43. Meat, in Psalm 42:3
46. Writer's deg.
47. Hamlet and kin
49. Kan. neighbor
52. Feared fly
55. Joseph and others (Genesis 37:5)
57. Meadow mom

60. Sailor's saint
64. New handle for Jacob (Genesis 32:28)
66. Wife of Ahasuerus
68. Consecrate with oil (Exodus 29:7–9)
70. Cain raised him (Genesis 4:17)
72. Questionable
74. "Let not the ___ down upon your wrath" (Ephesians 4:26)
75. Gabriel, for one (Luke 1:26)
76. Go it alone
77. The armour of God withstands this (Ephesians 6:13)
78. 1847 Melville novel
79. What is impossible to Dios? (Mark 10:27)
80. Wharton grads
81. Ripped apart
82. Saints' org.

1	2	3	4	5	■	6	7	8	9	10	■	11	12	13	14	15
16					■	17					■	18				
19					■	20					■	21				
22					23						24					■
■	25			■	26			■	■	27				■	■	■
■	■	■	28	29		■	30	31	32	■	33			34	35	36
37	38	39	■	40		41	■	42		43			■	44		
45			46				47				■	48	49			
50				■	51						52	■	53			
54				55	■	56						57				
58			■	59	60				■	61			■	62		
63			64			■	65		66	■	67		68	■	■	■
■	■	■	69			70	■	■	71	72		■	73	74	75	■
■	76	77					78	79				80				81
82					■	83					■	84				
85					■	86					■	87				
88					■	89					■	90				

Name That Tune

Across

1. Loll in the sun
5. Attach
11. Forster's *A ___ to India*
18. North Carolina college
19. Get to
20. Bliss
21. Read Exodus 9:1 and name that tune!
23. Former Haitian leader and physician, informally
24. "___ Mater" (hymn)
25. More pungent, in a way
27. Philosopher Descartes
28. Gentle touch
30. Craving
31. Satirical magazine
33. Read Luke 2:7 and name that tune!
40. Checking account selling feature
44. Crackers
45. Restauranteur Toots
46. Grain grinder
48. Club for country kids
50. Editor's "never mind"
52. Anklebones
53. Leg, slangily
54. Ring decisions (abbr)
56. Concerning
58. Hot pilots
60. Read Hebrews 11 and name that tune!
63. Person SW of China
64. Trillion: prefix
65. Where the disciple whom Jesus loved took Mary (John 19:27)
66. Heightened fuss
67. Utah city
69. Web destination
71. Passover's month
74. Made aggressive advances toward
77. Where the congregation meets
79. Actor Robert De ___
80. "And I will bring forth ___ out of Jacob" (Isaiah 65:9)
81. Read Deuteronomy 32:11 and name that tune!
84. Soap-making stuff
86. Number of lepers Jesus cured, in Luke's account (Luke 17:11–19)
87. RR stop
88. Landers and Sothern
91. Deepens a waterway
95. Tagged violent movies
100. Into reading
102. Read 1 Samuel 3 and name that tune!
104. Afternoon performance
105. Dior-shaped dress
106. Opera song
107. Seattle-based rock group
108. Sacred Hindu formula
109. Risque

Down

1. Pleads
2. "There was also ___ for the rest of the children of Manasseh" (Joshua 17:2)
3. Fountain order
4. Drawer part
5. Chinese card games
6. The Lord "hath shewed strength" with his ___, according to Mary's song (Luke 1:51)
7. Groups that abide by own rules (abbr)
8. "___ consummation devoutly..." *(Hamlet)*
9. Novelist Waugh
10. Cash in reserve
11. Romantic Le Pew of cartoons
12. "...sound an ___ in my holy mountain." (Joel 2:1)
13. Gullible one
14. Hollywood newcomer's dream
15. Auxiliary
16. Hired thug
17. Suffix for quality or state
22. Desert streambed
26. Stagnant
29. Scrooge's utterances
32. Liturgical verse
33. TV alien
34. Court a lady
35. Better than
36. Toy terrier, for short
37. Artistic theme
38. Retort to "Am too!"
39. Lariat
41. Includes, as in an estimate
42. Vigorous enthusiasms

43. Shade trees
47. Indolence
49. Rum warmer-upper
51. Accurate alignments
55. Belefonte or Lewis
57. Goofing up
59. Early space program
60. Veterinarian's patients, stereotypically
61. Bridge bid, briefly
62. Deathly
63. Novelist Janowitz
68. Three-card game
70. Nights before
72. Vocal disagreement (abbr)
73. CPAs crunch them
75. Leather from the sea
76. Boston suburb
78. *CHiPs* star Erik
82. Name in a Frank McCourt title
83. Summer forecast
85. Henry Ford's son
88. S.D.I. weapons
89. Prominent Genesis figure
90. "And should ___ spare Nineveh . . . ?" (Jonah 4:11)
92. Perlman of *Cheers*
93. Moran of *Happy Days*
94. Faxed, perhaps
96. Wing-shaped
97. When tripled, a 1970 WWII movie
98. Rock's Clapton
99. 6/6/44
101. " . . . or have ___ power to deliver?" (Isaiah 50:2)
103. Comparative suffix

DESCRIBE THAT WOMAN!

Across

1. Abate
5. "Here's where I'm ___ far" (progress report)
9. Full of: suffix
12. Swindle
17. The E in QED
18. Cleaving tool
19. Collection of sayings
20. Referee, slang
21. One description of Sarah
24. Dark orange-yellow
25. Do better at stealing bases, maybe
26. Sleeveless dress
28. Gov't hush-hush org.
29. Amy's husband in *Little Women*
31. New arrival's study (abbr)
32. "And it ___ to pass" (often-used Bible phrase)
36. One description of Ruth
39. Examination determining financial aid eligibility
43. Cushion sticker
44. Bring up
45. Land unit
46. Doughnut-shape
48. President between John and Richard
49. Is dry
53. Equal (with)
55. Biblical people in this puzzle
61. Become manifest
62. Pays to play
64. Dogpatch creator
68. Uneasy utterances
71. Spheric starter
72. Very slow tempo in music
73. Pasture
74. Ready for immediate action
78. One description of the Queen of Sheba
81. "Quien ___?" ("Who knows?" Sp.)
82. Bobby the Bruin
83. "Goodness gracious!"
84. "Gotcha!"
87. Strip that divides highway
89. Toddler's conveyance
91. Elk's place
95. One description of Esther
97. *Murder in the Cathedral* playwright
98. Chemical suffix
99. Dutch East Indian Empire founder
100. Gumbo ingredient
101. Minds
102. Docs
103. Word on a towel
104. Floridian islands

Down

1. "Victory is ours!"
2. His teachings were declared heresy at the Council of Nicaea
3. 1992 US-Can-Mex pact
4. Summers in France
5. Sworn statement giver
6. Malign
7. Most abstemious
8. Anthem contraction
9. *Magnum, P.I.* setting
10. The U in HUAC
11. Actor Will of *One Flew Over the Cuckoo's Nest*
12. Pre-1917 ruler
13. Skirt issue
14. ___ tide
15. "Blessed ___ the poor in spirit"
16. Sailor
22. Pueblo cooking pots
23. "I'm leaving on ___ plane"
27. Worker at North Pole
30. Analogy words
32. *The Godfather* actor
33. Gung-ho
34. Soybean paste
35. "And the Lord God planted a garden eastward in ___" (Genesis 2:8)
37. Express a view
38. Timber's downfall
39. Framer's border
40. Repeat
41. Seed cover
42. Unlikely prom king candidate
47. A star-crossed lover
48. Green frontage
50. Like kitchen trash cans, often
51. Fill in, at the office
52. St. Paul-to-St. Louis direction (abbr)
54. School group (abbr)
56. Jesus, notably
57. Turkish chiefs

58. Cruel
59. Calculated (abbr)
60. Desensitize
63. Photojournalism award since 1944
64. Politico Landon and others
65. Julie's role in *Doctor Zhivago*
66. For the infant Jesus, it was a manger
67. *A Death in the Family* author
69. Sanctus
70. Arctic footwear
73. Joseph Conrad title character
75. Stifle, as a grin
76. Australian salt lake
77. Both/either conjunctions
79. Female rabbit
80. Universally: prefix
84. Similar
85. Name of eight English kings
86. Geographic regions
87. Shea players
88. Overwhelms
90. "Hey, check that out!"
91. Allow
92. Grand ___ Opry
93. Racket
94. Creator of all things
96. Learning inst.

1	2	3	4	■	5	6	7	8	■	9	10	11	■	12	13	14	15	16
17				■	18				■	19			■	20				
21				22					23				■	24				
25								■	26				27		■	■	■	■
28			■	29				30		■	31			■	32	33	34	35
■	■	■	■	36						37				38				
39	40	41	42						■	43			■	44				
45				■	■	■	46		47			■	48					
49				50	51	52	■	■	53			54			■	■	■	■
■	55						56	57							58	59	60	■
■	■	■	■	61						■	■	62						63
64	65	66	67			■	68			69	70	■	■	■	71			
72					■	73			■	74		75	76	77				
78					79				80						■	■	■	■
81				■	82			■	83						■	84	85	86
■	■	■	■	87				88		■	89				90			
91	92	93	94		■	95				96								
97					■	98			■	99				■	100			
101					■	102				103				■	104			

To Err Is Human

Across

1. Get-go
6. Bacteria-inhibiting drug
11. Render useless
18. Apres-ski drink, maybe
19. Respiratory prefix
20. Ask
21. David's sin, for which he was forgiven (2 Samuel 11—12)
24. Rank
25. Commit a hocky no-no
26. Horse hoof sound
27. Pine
28. Turkish money
30. Like some seals
32. "I will put emnity between . . . thy seed and ___ seed" (Genesis 3:15)
33. Aaron and the Israelites' sin, for which they were forgiven (Exodus 32)
40. Sing a Christmas song
41. Singular
42. Leisurely walks
45. Intertwine
47. Darlings
50. " . . . and ___ down the wicked in their place" (Job 40:12)
51. Employ a rip cord
53. Arrangement containers
56. Once it rained for 40 of these
57. Theme of this puzzle
61. "He maketh the storm a ___" (Psalm 107:29)
65. Secure a gate
66. Island off Africa
71. "The best of them is as a ___" (Micah 7:4)
73. Taps the horn
76. "___ noches, senor!"
77. Dusk
80. Flesh
82. Lock
83. Peter's sin, for which he was forgiven (Matthew 26:69–75)
87. Cop's alert (abbr)
89. Blood vessel prefix
90. Jeanne d'Arc and Marie (abbr)
91. "___ a Woman" (Beatles' song)
93. Actress Teri of *Close Encounters of the Third Kind*
94. Deer
95. "Why ___ ye, ye high hills?" (Psalm 68:16)
99. Saul's sin, for which he was forgiven (Acts 9:1)
104. Stage role for a young woman
105. "There ___ atheists in a foxhole"
106. Conical kilns
107. Uses a microwave, maybe
108. Shea stadium occupant
109. Usurp forcefully

Down

1. "Beat it!"
2. Singer Amos
3. 43,560 square feet
4. Crowd's loud noise
5. Light brown
6. Exceptional
7. Pledge of Allegiance phrase
8. Romanian coin
9. Fido's coat
10. Garbed for certain liturgies
11. Removes antlers
12. Check out
13. Criterion (abbr)
14. Region
15. Seashore pest
16. Wood-shaping machine
17. Type of anesthetic
22. "___ the lily" (adorn unnecessarily)
23. Winglike parts
29. The best
31. Flit about
33. Scores a hole-in-one
34. Disagreeably moist
35. Air France destination
36. Passage
37. Charlton Heston epic
38. Get one's own apartment, say
39. Capitalized word in the King James Version
43. "Now I ___ me down to sleep"
44. Radical 1960s org.
46. Wicked
48. Collide (into)
49. U-turn from NNW
52. A Perón
54. Trauma centers, briefly
55. Sign of healing
58. Morticia's cousin
59. Sgt., e.g.

60. Adolescent
61. Cronkite's former employer
62. Indonesian islands
63. "The Lone Eagle" of 1944
64. Part of ancient Iran
67. Yukon, e.g. (abbr)
68. "Dedicated to the ___ Love"
69. Not fem. or neut.
70. To be: Lat.
72. *Class Reunion* novelist Jaffe
74. Della's angelic TV role
75. Semidry American white wine
78. Twistable tightener
79. Makes invalid
81. "The Waste Land" poet
84. Ominous
85. Naaman washed in it seven times (2 Kings 5)
86. Clucks disapprovingly
87. Out of bed
88. Cell ___
92. *Peter Pan* villain
95. Doesn't tell the truth
96. Relax
97. Tiny hill makers
98. "Hey. You. Yes, you!"
100. Bambi's aunt
101. Hue's partner
102. Haw's partner
103. Drag

THEY SAY THE DARNDEST THINGS

Across

1. Short
6. Can't hear
10. TV watchdog (abbr)
13. "Shoo!"
17. Relating to a grammatical form
18. A great distance
19. Mary Richards's TV boss
20. Den
21. Young Isaac's question, to Abraham (Genesis 22:7)
24. West Point (abbr)
25. God warned Noah of "things not ___ yet" (Hebrews 11:7)
26. Calms
27. Son of Noah (Genesis 5:32)
28. Life story, in short
30. Bruce or Laura of film
31. G-flat equivalent
33. Undefeated Rocky the boxer
38. Anchor Tom who wrote *The Greatest Generation*
40. Leaky radiator sound
41. Young Jesus' response, to Joseph and Mary (Luke 2:49)
44. Linen trimming tape
45. "Saint," in Brazil
46. Favorite
47. "I ___ pleasant bread" (Daniel 10:3)
50. Close-watch sys., at O'Hare
52. Schlepp
54. Landed properties
56. Cutting remark
59. What this puzzle features
63. Future attys' hurdle
64. Impaired in speech, as from a brain injury
66. Steinbeck's *Of Mice and ___*
67. Shoot a marble
69. ___ slow burn (seethes)
70. Python in Kipling's *The Jungle Book*
73. Rocker Ocasek
75. Diamond bags
79. Young Samuel's statement, to the Lord (1 Samuel 3:10)
83. Sound from a Jersey
85. What the psalmist asked to be purged with (Psalm 51:7)
86. It occurs around the 22nd of June and December
87. Duke Ellington's "Take the ___"
89. Furry *Star Wars* creature
91. Prevaricate
92. Abdominal region
93. Created a waterway through
96. Ruminant stomach's third chamber
101. Tress
102. Young David's promise, to Goliath (1 Samuel 17:46)
104. Israeli carrier
105. Composer Rorem
106. George Green's "Trompe d'___"
107. Sam of *Jurassic Park*
108. The "T" in TV
109. Gold border (abbr)
110. "Auld Lang ___"
111. Doctrine

Down

1. Car make (pl)
2. Architect Mies van der ___
3. ___ fixe (obsession)
4. Merit
5. Fido's banes
6. Court prosecutors (abbr)
7. Newts
8. Sighed with pleasure
9. *Cabaret* lyricist
10. Feature prohibiting approach, according to Leviticus 21:18
11. Sinatra's ___ *Blow Your Horn*
12. Chicago sports devotee, perhaps
13. Sloppy snow
14. Item on a balance sheet
15. Those about to shoot
16. Hoboes
22. Hoops Hall-of-Famer Thomas
23. Trounce
29. Singles
32. Kind of equity
33. Year of the World Trade Center airplane attack
34. Rand of *Atlas Shrugged*
35. D.C. stadium built in 1961
36. "Good-night Mrs. ___, wherever you are!" (Durante signoff)
37. Type of history collection under a specific letter
39. Passed a bad check
42. Garfield's *Body and ___*
43. Firm and resolute

48. Museum funding org.
49. East, in Essen
51. Slugger's stat
53. Precious stone
55. Mach 1 breaker
56. Rotten
57. G.I.'s address
58. Question not expecting a reply
60. Roosevelt's Secretary of the Interior
61. "Ol' Man River" composer
62. "... and everything ___ place"
65. Greet casually
68. Humiliation
71. Binary compound with a poisonous element
72. Open declaration
74. Gall prefix
76. Six, in Tuscany
77. "... yadda, yadda, yadda" (abbr)
78. Not he
80. Making simultaneous
81. New Testament evangelist
82. *Silas Marner* author George
83. Croquet need
84. Actor Peter of *Becket*
88. Joint between foot and leg
90. *One Flew Over the Cuckoo's Nest* author
94. "Madder than ___ hen"
95. Reverend's deg., perhaps
97. Suit to ___
98. Leg part
99. River to the Ubangi
100. Hot cheese
103. Capable of, suffix

OLDIES BUT GOODIES

Across

1. Poet-singer
5. Prefix with glyphic
10. Attendee
14. Score 100 percent
17. Fragrant wood
18. Thoroughly enjoy
19. Agitate
20. Soak
21. Hardly a spring chicken (Job 15:7)
24. Priest in 1 Samuel
25. Less audible
26. Done to ashes after cremation
27. 88-Down's father
29. Detroit product
31. Leather worker's tool
32. Some forensic evidence
33. Four-term president (abbr)
36. Cause of major irritation (2 Corinthians 12:7)
43. "Praise the Lord, all ye Gentiles; and ___ him" (Romans 15:11)
45. Blacksmith, often
46. Espionage org.
47. Magi's guide
48. Familiar phrase in marketing
50. Aggregate
51. Check for job application (abbr)
52. "___ will distress Ariel" (Isaiah 29:2)
53. Boll ___
55. Four: prefix
57. Successor of 33-Across (abbr)
59. Supply with people
60. Stretched to the limit, mentally (Psalm 107:27)
64. Friday or Preston (abbr)
67. ___ Jima
68. Greek ninth letter
69. Cooks' wear
73. Covers auto engine
75. MDs
77. "___ Yankee-Doodle Dandy"
79. Pope John Paul II's baptismal name
80. Grimm monster
81. Lennon's second
82. National pet lover's org.
84. Swain
85. Controlling group (Romans 13:1)
89. Electronic physicist Georg
90. Basic cable channel
91. Kin (abbr)
92. Capital of ancient Elam
94. Cleanse
97. Boston school (abbr)
100. Certain noblemen
104. "Blessed ___ the poor in spirit"
105. Inconsequential amount (Isaiah 40:15)
109. Number of silver pieces, in a parable (Luke 15:8)
110. Angora, for one
111. Govt. promissory note
112. Thatch overhang
113. How they looked on the way to Emmaus (Luke 24:17)
114. Tolkien creatures
115. "There is nothing like ___" (*South Pacific* lyric)
116. Imparts color

Down

1. Appeals to the Good Shepherd
2. Too
3. It's often over your head
4. Mouth of the Nile
5. Fireplace fronts
6. Flight rate (abbr)
7. Ides of March words
8. German industrial district
9. Like some concerts
10. Impossible traffic situation
11. What the foolish virgins lacked for their lamps
12. Building add-on
13. Plastics ingredients
14. Cruising
15. Soft drink
16. It's a long story
22. Bk. after Numbers
23. Cut, as wood
28. Fresh
30. Cries heard at fireworks displays
32. Scrolls site
33. Imperfection
34. Florida county
35. Cartoonist Goldberg
37. Mail carrier's beat
38. Arch rival
39. Draws near
40. News bit
41. Information

42. Word heard on March 17
44. Prima donna
49. Pasta choice
51. Like King James
54. Scoop
56. Ark animal unit
58. Toll rd.
61. Nary a soul
62. Home of Busch Gardens
63. Dreary
64. Worn-out
65. "Sunflowers" painter van ___
66. Sped
70. Cookie favorite since 1912
71. Methuselah's grandson
72. Squalid urban area
74. Profundity
76. Contaminates
78. Book written by Luke
82. Jimmy Carter Museum home
83. Like champagne, often
86. Tense
87. Big rig
88. Biblical twin
93. Like a rainbow
94. Nutso
95. Vicinity
96. Take care of
98. Right on a ship (abbr)
99. Branch of Islam
101. "Sure!"
102. Actress Cambell
103. Fr. holy women
106. Director Howard
107. Feedbag morsel
108. Shade tree

It's a Living

Across

1. Without
5. Pet lover's org.
9. Perch
12. The wood used to build David's house (2 Samuel 7:2)
17. Formal, legal document
18. Neaten, as a hedge
19. Former White House press secretary Fleischer
20. Don Ho's "hi"
21. Whit
22. "I'd like to ___ grievance with you!"
23. Newsman Koppel
24. Sought ore
25. Found on Jacob's kitchen table (Genesis 30)
28. They may be oral
29. Equator region, with "the"
30. Flowery necklace
31. Hindu honorific
32. Noah's favorite fees
39. Stopper
43. Holler
44. Snick and ___
45. Heroic narrative
46. Melodic
48. Mutual fund type (abbr)
50. First word in a Marx title
52. "Ouch!"
53. Phrase used in infomercials
55. Turkish chief
57. Ides of March words
59. Peter's favorite book
65. What Isaac wanted to do to Jacob's hands, to make sure he was Esau (Genesis 27:21)
66. Ancient metal collar
67. Incorporate
68. Not he
71. ___ Grande
72. Stead
74. John Wayne's ___ *of Iwo Jima*
75. Not theirs
77. Province north of Montana (abbr)
80. Isn't able to
82. Pinocchio's lie detector
83. Matthew's favorite Beatles lyric
87. "I ___ no pleasant bread." (Daniel 10:3)
88. Sailor's assent
89. Female reunion attendees
94. Strong greenish-blue
97. Joseph's favorite singers
100. Tabernacle curtain edges discussed in Exodus 26
101. Who receives monetary redemption? (Numbers 3:48)
102. Bo's'n's boss, short
103. Fortitude
104. Queen ___ Lace
105. Drunk
106. "Through thy precepts ___ understanding" (Psalm 119:104)
107. "Whoopee," to Titus
108. Martinez, Cy Young pitcher
109. Man behind the plate (abbr)
110. Box-office flops
111. Gels

Down

1. English satirist Jonathan
2. Loud, like a crowd
3. Part of TNT
4. "Smite with thine hand, and ___ with thy foot." (Ezekiel 6:11)
5. Like potatoes and bread
6. More prim and precise
7. Round (abbr)
8. Chinese nurse
9. Lustrous fabrics
10. "You won't have me to kick around anymore!"
11. Ocean movement
12. Kodak product
13. Medicine show purchases
14. Brazilian woman's title
15. "If I may interject something . . ."
16. X-ray doses
26. Sue Grafton's ___ *for Evidence*
27. Priest who reassured Hannah (1 Samuel 1:17)
31. Put away, as a sword
33. Fabric fold
34. Precarious situation
35. Yields
36. Astaire's *The ___ Divorcee*
37. Swelled head
38. "And I ___ a new heaven and a new earth" (Revelation 21:1)
39. School orgs.

40. Ness, for one
41. " . . . fear not to take ___ thee Mary thy wife." (Matthew 1:20)
42. Swindler, in Yiddish
47. Also-ran
49. Rel. study
51. Wine glass parts
54. First words in Micah 7
56. Egypt's continent
58. Word with renewal or sprawl
60. Parade attraction
61. Mountaineer's tool
62. Not stereo
63. Totals (up)
64. Financial page initials
68. Fermented beans
69. Shade
70. Memorable period
73. Like territory yet to be explored
76. More on the ball
78. Former kingdom of Iran
79. Excited
81. Money during Jesus' time
84. What "amen" means, essentially
85. Detective, slang
86. *The Flying* ___ (Sally Field role)
90. Homeowners pmts.
91. Chutzpah
92. Running amok
93. ___ Park, Colorado
94. Applaud
95. Top-of-the-line
96. Not quite a lake
97. Vegetarian staple
98. Biting, as in remark
99. Prego competitor

ANSWERS

Affirming God Forever (pp. 4–5)

A	N	N	A		L	E	A	H		S	T	A	L	L
B	O	O	N		I	L	I	A		K	O	R	E	A
A	V	I	D		F	O	R	T	H	I	N	E	I	S
C	A	S	T	L	E		S	C	U	D				
K	E	Y	H	O	L	E		H	A	D	A	S	A	Y
			E	X	I	L	E		C	O	N	N	I	E
P	R	O	P		K	A	N	E		O	D	O	R	S
A	E	R	O		E	T	O	N	S		T	R	E	E
C	R	O	W	N		E	C	T	O		H	E	S	S
T	U	N	E	I	N		H	E	N	C	E			
S	N	O	R	T	E	D		R	O	U	G	H	I	T
				P	O	O	R		F	E	L	I	N	E
T	H	E	K	I	N	G	D	O	M		O	R	A	N
R	E	L	I	C		M	A	T	A		R	E	N	O
I	N	I	N	K		A	S	O	N		Y	S	E	R

Bible Burgs (pp. 6–7)

C	A	I	N		F	A	S	T		R	A	J	A	H
O	H	N	O		E	C	H	O		E	N	E	M	Y
B	E	T	H	L	E	H	E	M		C	D	R	O	M
R	A	W		A	B	I	D	E	S		R	U	I	N
A	P	O	S	T	L	E	S		A	V	E	S		
			S	E	E	R		S	T	E	W	A	R	D
A	B	B	A				N	E	A	R		L	E	A
N	E	E		B	E	T	H	A	N	Y		E	N	D
N	E	T		E	V	I	L				A	M	O	S
E	P	H	R	A	I	M		T	O	R	I			
		S	E	N	T		H	E	R	O	D	I	A	S
L	E	A	P		A	N	E	M	I	A		M	C	I
A	L	I	E	N		C	A	P	E	R	N	A	U	M
D	I	D	N	T		A	T	T	N		A	G	R	O
D	E	A	T	H		A	S	S	T		M	E	A	N

Clothes Calls (pp. 8–9)

E	L	E	C	T		J	E	W	S		S	C	O	W
T	O	R	A	H		A	L	I	T		C	A	N	A
C	O	A	T	O	F	M	A	N	Y		A	M	E	S
H	M	S		M	E	E	T	S		F	L	E	S	H
			P	A	E	S	E		B	R	E	L		
F	E	W	E	S	T			B	L	E	S	S	E	D
L	A	H	R			S	C	O	U	T		H	B	O
E	R	I		C	O	L	O	U	R	S		A	E	R
A	T	T		O	R	A	N	T			F	I	R	M
S	H	E	C	H	E	M			H	E	A	R	T	S
		R	H	E	O		I	D	O	L	S			
A	D	O	R	N		G	O	U	R	D		S	L	O
B	I	B	I		L	I	N	E	N	E	P	H	O	D
E	V	E	S		O	N	I	T		R	O	U	N	D
L	A	S	T		T	A	C	O		S	I	N	G	S

Read All About It (pp. 10–11)

P	L	A	Y		B	A	B	A		D	R	E	S	S
R	U	L	E		A	V	O	W		R	O	D	E	O
U	N	I	T		S	O	L	O		A	B	N	E	R
D	A	V	I	D	K	I	L	L	S	G	I	A	N	T
E	R	E		R	E	D			T	O	N			
			E	A	T		E	D	E	N		C	P	A
S	H	A	R	K		A	M	E	N		T	O	O	L
H	E	B	R	E	W	S	C	R	O	S	S	S	E	A
O	R	E	S		A	H	E	M		W	A	T	T	S
W	E	T		S	K	Y	E		P	A	R			
			A	T	E			A	I	M		A	L	A
S	A	M	S	O	N	I	S	B	L	I	N	D	E	D
A	G	A	I	N		N	O	R	A		I	O	W	A
C	H	I	D	E		C	H	A	T		G	R	I	M
S	A	L	E	S		H	O	M	E		H	E	S	S

Plants in the Plan (pp. 12–13)

T	A	B	■	M	A	P	L	E	S	■	R	A	G	S
E	R	R	■	G	R	O	O	V	E	■	O	L	E	O
M	B	A	■	M	U	S	T	A	R	D	S	E	E	D
P	O	M	P	■	M	E	T	■	M	A	Y	■	■	■
O	R	B	I	T	■	D	O	F	O	R	■	B	A	D
■	■	L	E	A	P	■	■	O	N	E	T	I	M	E
O	L	E	■	P	E	T	E	R	■	D	E	T	E	R
L	O	B	E	■	P	U	R	G	E	■	E	T	N	A
L	A	U	D	S	■	N	A	O	M	I	■	E	S	T
A	T	S	T	A	K	E	■	■	S	O	A	R	■	■
S	H	H	■	B	A	R	N	S	■	U	S	H	E	R
■	■	■	S	O	Y	■	O	T	T	■	S	E	M	I
S	H	I	T	T	A	H	T	R	E	E	■	R	A	D
P	O	L	O	■	K	A	R	A	T	E	■	B	I	G
Y	E	L	P	■	S	W	E	D	E	N	■	S	L	Y

Angling with Angels (pp. 14–15)

A	L	P	H	A	■	L	E	V	I	■	G	O	S	H
S	P	E	A	R	■	I	L	E	D	■	A	C	H	Y
P	S	A	L	M	■	G	L	E	E	■	D	O	O	M
■	■	■	F	I	S	H	E	R	S	O	F	M	E	N
F	D	A	■	N	E	T	■	■	■	B	L	E	S	S
R	E	F	U	G	E	■	M	O	N	E	Y	■	■	■
A	M	O	S	■	■	S	E	A	T	S	■	P	E	I
Y	O	U	C	A	T	C	H	T	H	E	M	A	N	D
S	N	L	■	T	O	O	T	H	■	■	I	T	T	O
■	■	■	S	A	N	T	A	■	D	A	N	I	E	L
B	A	B	E	L	■	■	■	A	O	L	■	O	R	S
I	L	L	C	L	E	A	N	T	H	E	M	■	■	■
L	E	A	R	■	M	O	A	B	■	R	A	H	A	B
L	U	K	E	■	I	N	G	A	■	T	R	I	B	E
S	T	E	T	■	R	E	S	T	■	S	K	E	E	T

Three of Egypt's Plagues (pp. 16–17)

S	H	E	M	■	T	I	T	U	S	■	J	A	I	L
L	I	L	I	■	E	D	I	T	H	■	O	M	N	I
A	G	I	N	■	S	I	N	A	I	■	S	O	R	E
■	H	A	I	L	T	O	T	H	E	C	H	I	E	F
■	■	■	S	I	S	■	■	■	S	H	U	■	■	■
T	A	S	T	E	■	G	O	D	■	E	A	R	T	H
A	T	M	E	■	D	I	L	U	T	E	■	E	E	O
H	E	A	R	T	O	F	D	A	R	K	N	E	S	S
O	I	L	■	R	E	T	I	N	A	■	I	S	L	E
E	N	L	A	I	■	S	E	E	■	S	T	E	A	D
■	■	■	N	O	R	■	■	■	E	S	P	■	■	■
F	R	O	G	S	A	N	D	S	N	A	I	L	S	■
L	O	V	E	■	H	E	R	O	D	■	C	A	I	N
A	B	E	L	■	A	A	N	D	E	■	K	I	L	O
P	E	N	S	■	B	R	O	A	D	■	S	N	O	W

Bible Fauna (pp. 18–19)

S	H	E	E	P	■	S	W	A	N	■	S	P	A	S
A	U	R	A	E	■	C	O	M	O	■	W	E	L	T
T	E	R	R	A	■	O	R	E	O	■	A	R	G	O
■	■	■	■	C	A	T	E	R	P	I	L	L	A	R
C	H	A	M	O	I	S	■	■	■	S	L	E	E	K
R	E	D	U	C	E	■	G	E	T	T	O	■	■	■
A	L	A	R	K	■	E	A	R	T	H	W	O	R	M
W	I	N	■	■	F	L	I	N	T	■	■	Z	O	E
S	C	O	R	P	I	O	N	S	■	S	H	O	V	E
■	■	■	O	A	S	I	S	■	S	P	I	N	E	T
A	B	H	O	R	■	■	■	B	E	A	V	E	R	S
G	R	A	S	S	H	O	P	P	E	R	■	■	■	■
L	I	N	T	■	O	R	A	L	■	R	A	V	E	N
O	B	O	E	■	P	E	R	U	■	O	L	I	V	E
W	E	I	R	■	E	L	K	S	■	W	I	P	E	D

Answers

Kinswoman (pp. 20–21)

A	S	I		D	I	S	C	O		A	M	O	E	B	A	S
I	N	N		E	A	T	O	N		P	A	V	L	O	V	A
R	E	A		A	N	A	M	E		B	L	E	S	S	E	D
B	E	S	O	T		T	E	A	L		I	N	E	S	S	E
A	R	T	T	H	O	U	A	M	O	N	G					
G	A	I	T		D	E	G		S	I	N	C	L	A	I	R
S	T	R	O	K	E		A	H	E	M		H	E	N	C	E
				N	O	L	I	E		B	L	O	T	T	E	D
	W	O	M	E	N	A	N	D	B	L	E	S	S	E	D	
W	A	R	I	E	S	T		G	E	E	S	E				
I	S	A	L	L		H	E	E	D		S	N	O	R	E	D
S	A	L	E	S	M	E	N		F	E	E		D	A	D	E
					I	S	T	H	E	F	R	U	I	T	O	F
I	T	H	A	C	A		S	E	L	F		S	E	T	M	E
T	H	Y	W	O	M	B		A	L	E	P	H		L	I	N
H	E	D	O	N	I	C		L	O	T	T	E		E	T	S
E	Y	E	L	E	S	S		S	W	E	A	R		S	E	E

Hidden Word (pp. 22–23)

D	U	S	T	S		B	O	A	T	S		P	I	E	T	A
I	N	T	H	E		E	N	L	A	I		H	O	V	E	R
S	P	A	R	E		L	E	A	S	T		I	N	A	N	E
C	O	L	O	S	S	I	A	N	S		P	L	A	N	T	S
S	T	E	N		S	E	L		E	D	G	E		S	S	T
			E	A	R	S		G	L	E	A	M	S			
P	A	R	S	E			M	E	S	S		O	N	I	C	E
A	W	E		R	O	B	O	T		E	U	N	U	C	H	S
C	A	R	B		N	U	M	B	E	R	S		G	A	I	T
T	R	U	M	P	E	T		U	T	T	E	R		N	N	E
S	E	N	O	R		T	E	S	S			A	L	T	A	R
			C	O	M	I	T	Y		S	A	S	E			
W	E	D		V	I	N	E		A	T	O		T	A	P	E
I	N	E	V	E	R		R	E	V	E	L	A	T	I	O	N
S	O	F	A	R		I	N	D	I	A		R	E	M	I	T
P	L	A	N	B		C	A	N	A	L		E	R	A	S	E
S	A	T	E	S		C	L	A	N	S		A	S	T	E	R

Dynamic Duos (pp. 24–25)

S	I	R	E	D		B	I	S	E	C	T		T	U	F	T
I	S	I	T	I		E	S	C	R	O	W		O	N	E	A
R	U	T	H	A	N	D	N	A	O	M	I		A	F	A	R
S	P	E	E	D	Y		T	R	I	M				A	R	P
			L	E	L	A		E	C	U	A		G	I	N	O
L	A	P		M	O	S	E	S	A	N	D	A	A	R	O	N
O	C	R			N	I	N			E	A	R	N			
R	H	O	D	A		G	I	B	B		S	E	D	G	E	
D	A	V	I	D	A	N	D	B	A	T	H	S	H	E	B	A
	T	O	N	E	R		S	A	R	I		T	I	N	E	S
			A	L	E	E			I	T	S			I	R	A
L	E	A	H	A	N	D	R	A	C	H	E	L		E	T	S
O	L	E	S		A	U	E	L		E	V	E	S			
V	I	N				C	D	L	I		E	A	T	E	T	H
E	X	E	S		J	A	C	O	B	A	N	D	E	S	A	U
M	I	A	S		A	I	O	N	A	L		M	E	A	L	S
E	R	S	T		S	E	D	E	R	S		E	R	I	C	H

Famous Phrases (pp. 26–27)

S	A	F	E	R		S	L	E	W		M	A	N	G	E	R
O	R	A	T	E		T	E	R	I		E	L	A	P	S	E
U	R	I	A	H		A	C	T	S		T	O	S	S	E	D
S	A	L	T	O	F	T	H	E	E	A	R	T	H			
A	Y	S		B	A	S			M	A	O			A	F	B
			C	O	W		R	O	A	R		A	U	D	I	O
		C	H	A	N	G	E	O	N	E	S	S	P	O	T	S
G	R	I	M	M		A	S	P			H	E	A	R	T	S
O	A	S			B	L	T		A	B	A			N	E	E
A	T	T	I	R	E			I	C	E		H	E	E	D	S
T	H	E	F	A	T	O	F	T	H	E	L	A	N	D		
E	E	R	I	E		B	I	T	E		O	N	O			
E	R	N			T	O	G			A	D	D		M	O	S
			G	I	V	E	U	P	T	H	E	G	H	O	S	T
D	E	M	O	N	S		R	O	W	E		R	O	U	S	E
A	T	O	N	C	E		E	L	I	A		I	N	N	I	E
H	E	I	G	H	T		S	E	N	D		P	E	T	E	R

And the Hits Just . . . (pp. 28–29)

C	H	I	M	E	S	■	H	I	L	L	S	■	S	T	A	B
H	O	N	E	S	T	■	O	N	E	I	N	■	P	O	R	K
I	N	C	A	S	E	■	O	S	A	K	A	■	E	L	M	S
L	E	A	D	E	R	O	F	T	H	E	P	A	C	K	■	■
E	S	S	E	N	■	A	S	S	■	N	U	R	S	E	R	Y
■	■	■	■	C	C	S	■	■	W	E	P	T	■	I	F	A
M	O	T	H	E	R	I	N	L	A	W	■	H	A	N	D	Y
I	N	R	E	■	O	S	I	E	R	■	R	U	G	■	■	■
S	A	U	N	A	S	■	P	A	D	■	E	R	A	S	E	S
■	■	■	R	R	S	■	P	S	E	U	D	■	I	S	O	N
S	E	E	Y	A	■	J	O	H	N	N	Y	A	N	G	E	L
I	V	S	■	B	R	A	N	■	■	D	E	L	■	■	■	■
R	E	Q	U	I	E	M	■	I	C	I	■	D	E	F	A	T
■	■	U	N	C	H	A	I	N	E	D	M	E	L	O	D	Y
P	A	I	D	■	A	I	D	E	D	■	E	N	T	R	A	P
O	G	R	E	■	S	C	O	R	E	■	S	T	O	G	I	E
P	E	E	R	■	H	A	L	T	S	■	S	E	N	O	R	S

Gospel Writers (pp. 30–31)

■	M	U	L	E	S	■	A	H	I	G	H	■	E	B	B	S
T	O	N	I	T	E	■	S	O	N	I	A	■	S	A	R	I
M	A	T	T	H	E	W	P	E	R	R	Y	■	O	P	E	N
S	N	O	■	A	S	H	■	■	I	D	E	S	■	T	E	L
■	■	■	A	N	T	I	C	S	■	■	S	T	R	I	D	E
A	M	E	N	■	■	R	E	A	L	M	■	O	O	Z	E	S
M	A	R	K	E	T	R	E	S	E	A	R	C	H	E	R	S
O	C	T	A	V	O	■	■	S	T	R	I	K	E	■	■	■
N	E	E	■	I	S	N	O	■	A	M	O	S	■	A	L	A
■	■	■	S	L	E	A	Z	E	■	■	D	U	S	T	I	N
L	U	K	E	W	A	R	M	R	E	C	E	P	T	I	O	N
A	K	I	T	A	■	C	A	R	T	A	■	■	E	T	N	A
Z	E	P	H	Y	R	■	■	S	E	D	A	N	S	■	■	■
A	L	L	■	S	A	L	T	■	■	D	U	O	■	O	P	S
R	E	I	D	■	J	O	H	N	N	Y	J	U	M	P	U	P
U	L	N	A	■	A	N	E	Y	E	■	U	S	A	R	M	Y
S	E	G	S	■	S	I	N	E	W	■	S	E	E	Y	A	■

Landmark Decisions (pp. 32–33)

A	L	A	M	P	■	D	R	E	D	G	E	■	A	V	A	■
W	I	R	E	R	■	E	N	T	I	R	E	■	L	A	S	H
L	A	N	D	O	F	C	A	N	A	A	N	■	I	L	K	A
S	T	E	E	P	L	E	■	A	L	P	■	O	G	L	E	R
■	■	■	S	H	O	N	E	■	S	H	E	P	H	E	R	D
W	A	G	■	E	A	T	A	T	■	S	L	A	T	Y	■	■
H	E	A	R	S	T	■	R	A	T	■	A	R	S	O	N	S
A	R	R	A	Y	■	E	N	C	H	A	N	T	■	F	E	E
L	A	D	E	■	C	D	E	■	E	N	D	■	A	S	W	E
E	T	E	■	W	A	Y	S	I	D	E	■	P	S	A	L	M
S	E	N	T	O	N	■	T	O	E	■	B	A	L	L	O	T
■	■	O	R	O	N	O	■	R	E	C	U	R	■	T	W	O
L	I	F	E	L	O	N	G	■	P	A	E	A	N	■	■	■
A	R	E	A	S	■	C	R	Y	■	U	N	B	O	U	N	D
L	A	D	D	■	S	E	A	O	F	G	A	L	I	L	E	E
O	N	E	O	■	P	I	S	G	A	H	■	E	R	N	I	E
■	I	N	N	■	A	S	S	I	S	T	■	S	E	A	L	S

Taking Flight (pp. 34–35)

S	A	G	A	S	■	A	L	I	B	A	B	A	■	S	P	A
A	R	O	M	A	■	L	A	N	O	L	I	N	■	T	E	L
L	E	T	M	Y	P	E	O	P	L	E	G	O	■	O	R	D
S	C	H	O	O	L	■	■	U	A	E	■	I	O	N	I	A
A	A	S	■	N	A	M	E	R	S	■	A	N	G	E	L	S
■	■	■	H	A	N	A	N	I	■	E	C	T	O	■	■	■
■	■	P	A	R	T	E	D	T	H	E	R	E	D	S	E	A
H	A	I	F	A	■	■	■	Y	O	K	E	D	■	P	A	L
A	B	E	T	■	S	P	Y	■	E	S	S	■	T	E	R	M
L	I	T	■	E	L	F	I	N	■	■	■	O	R	A	L	S
F	E	A	S	T	O	F	P	A	S	S	O	V	E	R	■	■
■	■	■	W	H	A	T	■	P	L	A	N	E	S	■	■	■
I	N	V	A	I	N	■	S	H	O	W	E	R	■	D	R	S
P	I	A	N	O	■	E	A	T	■	■	I	A	G	R	E	E
R	T	S	■	P	I	L	L	A	R	O	F	C	L	O	U	D
A	R	E	■	I	N	S	O	L	E	S	■	T	E	N	S	E
Y	E	S	■	A	N	A	N	I	A	S	■	S	N	E	E	R

Answers

Paradise Lost . . . (pp. 36–37)

R	E	A	L	M			S	W	A	P		G	R	A	S	
A	T	R	I	A		S	H	E	B	A		R	A	S	H	
T	H	E	S	N	A	K	E	P	I	T		O	W	N	E	D
S	E	E		S	U	E		T	R	O	T		W	A	L	E
O	R	D	A	I	N	E	D		D	I	S	C	I	P	L	E
			D	O	T	T	E	D		S	H	A	N			
S	A	T	A	N	S		N	O	G		I	N	D	E	E	P
A	T	O	M	S		B	A	Z	A	A	R		I	N	L	A
R	I	T	A		T	E	R		T	E	T		N	O	T	I
A	M	A	N		H	E	I	F	E	R		T	E	T	O	N
H	E	L	D	T	O		I	A	L		A	R	D	E	N	T
			E	Z	R	A		D	E	C	R	E	E			
H	E	A	V	E	N	L	Y		G	L	E	A	N	I	N	G
A	L	D	A		S	T	A	B		U	S	S		G	A	O
L	A	D	L	E		A	L	L	A	B	O	U	T	E	V	E
	T	O	Y	S		R	I	O	T	S		R	A	T	E	S
	E	N	N	E		S	E	T	A			E	X	A	L	T

Cross Swords (pp. 38–39)

W	E	L	L		F	A	S	T	E	D		M	O	C	H	A
A	L	E	E		O	R	T	E	G	A		O	O	H	E	D
K	I	N	G	S	O	L	O	M	O	N		S	N	E	A	D
E	D	D	I	E		O	P	P		C	S	A		E	V	E
D	E	S	O	T	O			T	H	E	W	I	C	K	E	D
			N	A	K	E	D		E	R	I	C	A			
U	R	L	S		I	L	E		M	S	T		M	A	N	O
L	E	O		I	N	L	A	W				H	E	R	O	D
T	H	E	A	N	G	E	L	O	F	T	H	E	L	O	R	D
R	A	W	L	S				E	L	I	A	S		S	S	E
A	B	E	L		I	S	R		E	T	V		S	E	E	R
			A	O	R	T	A		D	O	O	D	Y			
R	A	S	H	W	O	R	D	S			C	A	R	M	E	L
I	N	T		N	N	E		I	B	E		D	I	A	R	Y
P	E	A	C	E		A	R	M	O	R	B	E	A	R	E	R
E	R	R	O	R		M	O	B	I	L	E		N	I	C	E
R	A	S	P	S		S	E	A	L	E	D		S	E	T	S

The Miracle Worker (pp. 40–41)

F	E	A	R		A	R	I	C	H		A	L	A	R	M	
I	N	R	E		M	A	C	A	O		C	E	R	E	A	L
F	E	E	D	S	T	H	E	M	U	L	T	I	T	U	D	E
T	R	A	C	E			S	E	R	E			E	S	A	I
H	O	S	A	N	N	A		O	W	N	E	D		E	T	A
			P	O	E	M	S		A	D	D	O	N			
S	A	P		R	A	I	S	E	S	L	A	Z	A	R	U	S
O	D	E	S		R	E	G	D			M	E	D	I	N	A
F	E	R	M	I		S	T	I	L	L		R	I	V	A	L
E	L	I	O	T	S			T	E	A	L		A	E	R	O
W	A	L	K	S	O	N	T	H	E	S	E	A		R	M	N
			E	A	S	Y	A		R	E	A	D	D			
C	O	M		T	O	M	B	S		D	R	E	A	M	E	D
A	M	A	N			P	L	E	D			E	R	A	T	O
M	A	K	E	S	T	H	E	W	A	T	E	R	W	I	N	E
P	H	O	B	I	A		T	U	T	O	R		I	N	A	S
	A	S	O	N	G		S	P	E	A	R		N	E	S	T

Service Stations (pp. 42–43)

	S	L	I	M		B	A	A	L		T	O	T	A	L	
E	T	U	D	E		A	N	D	I		A	R	A	B	I	A
C	E	C	I	L		P	G	A	S		L	A	B	A	N	S
H	E	R	O	D	S	T	E	M	P	L	E		E	T	E	S
O	R	E	M		O	I	L	S		E	N	T	R	E	A	T
			S	E	U	S	S		S	A	T	A	N			
O	A	K		E	L	M		E	O	N		R	A	B	B	I
F	L	A	S	K	S		I	N	N	O			C	E	R	F
A	T	T	Y	S		A	D	D	O	N		C	L	E	A	T
R	A	I	N			L	O	A	F		Q	U	E	N	C	H
C	R	E	A	M		B	L	T		G	U	S		E	E	E
			G	O	D	I	S		N	O	A	H	S			
S	O	L	O	M	O	N		D	O	F	F		H	A	N	A
P	R	O	G		T	O	W	E	R	O	F	B	A	B	E	L
E	N	D	U	R	E		E	B	E	R		A	D	O	V	E
D	O	G	E	A	R		E	R	S	T		B	O	D	E	S
	T	E	S	T	S		P	A	T	H		E	W	E	R	

When There's a Will (pp. 44–45)

F	I	E	F	S		B	E	G	I	N		M	A	S	T	S
A	C	U	R	E		A	S	I	D	E		I	G	L	O	O
L	A	B	O	R		N	A	M	E	S		K	N	O	W	N
C	L	I	M	B	E	D	U	P	A	T	R	E	E			
O	L	E	M	I	S	S		S	L	E	W		W	H	A	M
				A	T	T	A		S	R	A	S		I	L	O
E	G	A	L		H	A	L	O		S	N	O	W	S	I	N
S	O	D	A	S		N	O	D	E		D	A	I	S	E	S
T	O	U	C	H	E	D	H	I	S	G	A	R	M	E	N	T
A	I	L	E	E	N		A	U	T	O		S	P	R	E	E
T	E	A	R	S	A	T		M	E	D	E		Y	S	E	R
E	S	T		A	M	E	N		E	F	T	S				
S	T	E	S		O	N	E	A		A	C	E	T	A	T	E
			T	H	R	O	U	G	H	T	H	E	R	O	O	F
C	A	S	E	Y		U	R	I	A	H		D	I	R	E	R
B	R	E	E	D		R	O	L	L	E		E	N	T	R	E
S	T	A	L	E		S	N	E	E	R		R	E	A	R	M

Passion Week (pp. 46–47)

B	E	R	T	H		P	A	R	A	B	L	E		M	E	T
A	M	O	R	Y		A	N	D	I	R	O	N		A	L	E
J	U	D	A	S	I	S	C	A	R	I	O	T		S	I	E
A	S	S	I	S	T	S				A	N	S	P	A	C	H
			L	O	T		A	S	S	N			I	D	I	E
S	A	G		P	O	N	T	I	U	S	P	I	L	A	T	E
A	G	A	S			O	O	Z	E		E	C	G			
L	A	S	T	S	U	P	P	E	R		S	A	R	G	E	S
A	P	P	E	A	S	E				C	O	R	I	N	T	H
D	E	S	I	R	E		G	E	T	H	S	E	M	A	N	E
			N	A	N		A	C	R	E			S	T	A	B
C	R	O	W	N	O	F	T	H	O	R	N	S		S	S	A
Y	U	M	A			A	S	O	N		U	P	C			
P	L	A	Y	A	C	T				E	N	R	A	G	E	S
R	E	N		S	I	M	O	N	O	F	C	Y	R	E	N	E
U	R	I		S	T	A	R	E	A	T		E	L	T	O	N
S	S	S		T	E	N	D	E	R	S		R	O	A	S	T

The Rainmaker (pp. 48–49)

H	A	L	F		R	O	B	E	D		M	A	L	I	C	E
E	L	O	I		A	H	O	L	E		T	R	I	B	E	S
R	O	D	E		G	O	D	S	C	O	V	E	N	A	N	T
B	U	I	L	D	T	H	E	A	R	K			E	R	T	E
			D	U	O			S	Y	R	I	A	N			
D	A	S		E	P	I	C			A	S	L		V	O	W
A	D	A	M	S		S	O	L	I		B	I	K	I	N	I
N	E	B	O		I	N	H	I	M		O	B	E	R	O	N
		B	U	R	N	T	O	F	F	E	R	I	N	G		
P	L	A	N	E	T		R	E	R	A	N		D	I	R	T
B	A	T	T	L	E		T	R	E	S		J	O	N	A	H
A	S	H		A	N	T			E	E	R	O		S	P	Y
			E	X	T	R	A	S			O	U	T			
A	L	E	X			O	L	I	V	E	B	R	A	N	C	H
R	A	V	E	N	A	N	D	D	O	V	E		R	A	R	E
O	S	I	R	I	S		A	L	T	A	R		E	D	O	M
D	E	L	T	A	S		S	E	E	S	T		S	A	P	S

Run for Your Lives (pp. 50–51)

S	H	O	W		H	E	R	A			M	I	D	S	T	S
M	A	L	I		A	M	I	N	O		I	D	O	T	O	O
O	R	I	N		S	E	P	I	A		S	O	M	E	R	S
G	I	V	E	S	A	U	L	T	H	E	S	L	I	P		
		E	L	O			E	A	U	X		A	N	I	N	
C	H	O	I	R	B	O	Y			P	A	T	I	N	A	E
H	A	Y	S	E	E	D		H	O	T	F	O	O	T	I	T
G	I	L	T		N	O	P	A	R		A	R	N	O	L	D
					C	R	O	W	B	A	R					
M	U	L	I	S	H		G	E	S	S	O		M	R	E	D
F	R	O	M	H	E	R	O	D		I	F	F	I	E	S	T
D	I	S	P	O	S	E			O	F	F	E	N	S	E	S
	S	T	O	W		E	T	C	H			T	E	T		
		F	L	E	E	F	R	O	M	P	H	A	R	A	O	H
C	L	A	I	R	E		A	P	I	L	E		A	T	M	E
P	A	C	T	E	N		Y	A	S	I	R		L	E	A	N
S	P	E	E	D	Y			Y	S	E	R		S	S	R	S

ANSWERS

He Is Risen! (pp. 52–53)

A	G	A	S	S	I		O	F	S	I	N	S		S	I	S
I	N	G	M	A	R		D	E	A	R	I	E		E	S	T
M	A	R	Y	M	A	G	D	A	L	E	N	E		R	O	E
	T	A	R	S		O	S	S	O			S	L	A	V	E
			N	O	T	I		T	M	A	N		O	P	E	L
	P	L	A	N	O	N		S	E	P	U	L	C	H	R	E
D	I	E		S	O	G	O			B	L	E	U			
E	V	A	H		T	T	O	P	S			I	S	A	L	L
J	O	S	E	P	H	O	F	A	R	I	M	A	T	H	E	A
A	T	T	A	R			S	P	A	N	O		S	O	A	S
			V	O	I	D			S	A	N	G		S	S	S
A	S	C	E	N	S	I	O	N		W	E	A	L	T	H	
M	E	O	N		H	O	P	E		E	L	L	E			
A	R	I	S	E			E	X	P	O		I	G	O	T	
Z	E	N		M	O	U	N	T	O	F	O	L	I	V	E	S
E	N	E		I	S	L	E	T	S		R	E	O	I	L	S
D	A	D		T	H	E	D	O	T		R	E	N	D	E	R

The Stones' Greatest Hits (pp. 54–55)

C	R	O	S	S		M	O	S	E	S		A	D	A	M	S
L	U	N	C	H		O	N	E	T	O		N	A	G	A	T
E	M	C	E	E		R	A	N	O	N		T	H	I	N	E
F	O	U	N	D	A	T	I	O	N		P	I	L	L	O	W
T	R	E	E		B	A	R	R		T	O	O		E	R	S
			R	I	A	L		A	D	V	I	C	E			
L	L	O	Y	D			U	S	E	S		H	A	M	S	
I	A	M		B	U	R	N		A	H	A		R	I	I	S
E	B	E	N	E	Z	E	R		C	O	V	E	N	A	N	T
N	O	G	O		I	N	E		O	W	E	D		P	A	U
	R	A	V	I		D	A	W	N			A	G	A	I	N
			A	N	G	E	L	A		L	A	M	A			
S	S	A		F	A	R		V	E	I	L		L	I	K	E
C	E	P	H	A	S		D	E	N	O	F	L	I	O	N	S
A	V	I	A	N		A	A	R	O	N		A	L	T	O	S
L	E	A	S	T		S	T	E	L	E		P	E	A	C	E
A	N	N	A	S		P	E	D	A	L		D	E	S	K	S

Render unto Caesar (pp. 56–57)

D	O	T	H		E	L	F	I	N		V	I	P	E	R	S
I	N	R	E		V	O	I	C	E		A	D	A	G	E	S
S	E	A	L		E	N	D	O	W		S	T	R	O	B	E
C	O	M	M	U	N	I	O	N	B	R	E	A	D			
O	N	S	E	T				S	I	C		G	O	B	A	D
			T	A	S	T	E		E	M	T			E	D	U
N	I	P	S		E	R	A	S		P	A	S	S	T	H	E
U	N	A		H	E	A	R	T	S		C	A	C	H	E	D
M	E	T	O	O		P	L	A	T	E		T	I	A	R	A
B	R	I	E	R	S		S	L	A	V	E	S		N	E	T
E	T	E	R	N	A	L		K	R	E	S		H	Y	D	E
R	I	N			D	U	B		E	L	S	I	E			
S	A	T	E	D		R	A	H				S	A	V	O	R
			R	E	V	E	N	U	E	S	E	R	V	I	C	E
P	I	L	A	T	E		A	R	R	O	W		E	T	O	N
C	L	O	S	E	T		N	O	I	S	E		N	A	M	E
S	E	W	E	R	S		A	N	N	A	S		S	L	E	W

Circuit Riders (pp. 58–59)

S	A	T	A	N		T	R	I	B	E		S	C	O	N	E
C	L	O	V	E		E	A	S	E	S		W	O	R	L	D
O	P	R	A	H		E	C	L	A	T		I	N	S	E	T
W	H	A	T	I	S	T	H	E	T	E	R	M	F	O	R	
	A	H	A		C	H	E			S	O	M	E			
			R	A	H		L	P	S		M	A	R	C	O	S
T	S	K		L	E	E		R	A	T	E	S		A	N	T
A	H	O	M	I	L	Y	D	O	N	E		K	N	E	E	L
S	E	R	F		L	E	A	P	T	A	T		E	S	A	U
T	R	E	A	D		O	N	H	O	R	S	E	B	A	C	K
E	P	A		R	E	N	E	E		S	E	W		R	T	E
D	A	N	I	E	L		S	T	E		T	E	A			
			S	A	M	E			S	S	S		N	S	A	
	S	E	R	M	O	N	O	N	T	H	E	M	O	U	N	T
N	O	V	A	E		O	M	A	H	A		B	I	N	G	O
F	L	I	E	R		C	O	D	E	D		A	N	G	E	R
L	O	L	L	S		H	O	A	R	Y		S	T	O	L	E

Name That Tune (pp. 60–61)

B	A	S	K		F	A	S	T	E	N		P	A	S	S	A	G	E
E	L	O	N		A	R	R	I	V	E		E	L	A	T	I	O	N
G	O	D	O	W	N	M	O	S	E	S		P	A	P	A	D	O	C
S	T	A	B	A	T		S	A	L	T	I	E	R		R	E	N	E
				D	A	B			Y	E	N		M	A	D			
A	W	A	Y	I	N	A	M	A	N	G	E	R		N	O	F	E	E
L	O	C	O		S	H	O	R		G	R	I	S	T	M	I	L	L
F	O	U	R	H		S	T	E	T		T	A	L	I		G	A	M
		T	K	O	S		I	N	R	E		T	O	P	G	U	N	S
	F	A	I	T	H	O	F	O	U	R	F	A	T	H	E	R	S	
T	I	B	E	T	A	N		T	E	R	A		H	O	M	E		
A	D	O		O	R	E	M		S	I	T	E		N	I	S	A	N
M	O	V	E	D	I	N	O	N		N	A	V	E		N	I	R	O
A	S	E	E	D		O	N	E	A	G	L	E	S	W	I	N	G	S
			L	Y	E		T	E	N			S	T	A				
A	N	N	S		D	R	E	D	G	E	S		R	R	A	T	E	D
B	O	O	K	I	S	H		H	E	R	E	I	A	M	L	O	R	D
M	A	T	I	N	E	E		A	L	I	N	E	D		A	R	I	A
S	H	I	N	O	L	A		M	A	N	T	R	A		R	A	C	Y

Describe That Woman! (pp. 62–63)

W	A	N	E		A	T	S	O		O	U	S		C	H	E	A	T
E	R	A	T		F	R	O	E		A	N	A		Z	E	B	R	A
W	I	F	E	O	F	A	B	R	A	H	A	M		A	M	B	E	R
O	U	T	S	L	I	D	E		J	U	M	P	E	R				
N	S	A		L	A	U	R	I	E		E	S	L		C	A	M	E
				A	N	C	E	S	T	O	R	O	F	D	A	V	I	D
M	E	A	N	S	T	E	S	T		P	I	N		R	A	I	S	E
A	C	R	E				T	O	R	I	C		L	Y	N	D	O	N
T	H	I	R	S	T	S			O	N	A	P	A	R				
	O	L	D	T	E	S	T	A	M	E	N	T	W	O	M	E	N	
				E	M	E	R	G	E			A	N	T	E	S	U	P
A	L	C	A	P	P		U	H	O	H	S				A	T	M	O
L	A	R	G	O		L	E	A		O	N	S	T	A	N	D	B	Y
F	R	I	E	N	D	O	F	S	O	L	O	M	O	N				
S	A	B	E		O	R	R		M	Y	W	O	R	D		A	H	A
				M	E	D	I	A	N		S	T	R	O	L	L	E	R
L	O	D	G	E		J	E	W	I	S	H	H	E	R	O	I	N	E
E	L	I	O	T		I	N	E		C	O	E	N		O	K	R	A
T	E	N	D	S		M	D	S		H	E	R	S		K	E	Y	S

To Err Is Human (pp. 64–65)

S	T	A	R	T		S	U	L	F	A		D	I	S	A	B	L	E
C	O	C	O	A		P	N	E	U	M		E	N	T	R	E	A	T
A	R	R	A	N	G	E	D	U	R	I	A	H	S	D	E	A	T	H
T	I	E	R		I	C	E			C	L	O	P		A	C	H	E
					L	I	R	A		E	A	R	E	D		H	E	R
A	D	O	R	E	D	A	G	O	L	D	E	N	C	A	L	F		
C	A	R	O	L		L	O	N	E			S	T	R	O	L	L	S
E	N	L	A	C	E		D	E	A	R	S			T	R	E	A	D
S	K	Y	D	I	V	E			V	A	S	E	S		D	A	Y	S
				D	I	V	I	N	E	M	E	R	C	Y				
C	A	L	M		L	A	T	C	H			S	A	O	T	O	M	E
B	R	I	E	R			T	O	O	T	S		B	U	E	N	A	S
S	U	N	D	O	W	N			M	E	A	T		T	R	E	S	S
		D	E	N	I	E	D	J	E	S	U	S	T	H	R	I	C	E
A	P	B		A	N	G	I	O		S	T	E	S					
S	H	E	S		G	A	R	R			E	L	K		L	E	A	P
T	O	R	M	E	N	T	E	D	C	H	R	I	S	T	I	A	N	S
I	N	G	E	N	U	E		A	R	E	N	O		O	A	S	T	S
R	E	H	E	A	T	S		N	Y	M	E	T		W	R	E	S	T

They Say the Darndest . . . (pp. 66–67)

B	R	I	E	F		D	E	A	F		F	C	C		S	C	A	T
M	O	D	A	L		A	F	A	R		L	O	U		L	A	I	R
W	H	E	R	E	I	S	T	H	E	L	A	M	B		U	S	M	A
S	E	E	N	A	S		S	E	D	A	T	E	S		S	H	E	M
				B	I	O		D	E	R	N		F	S	H	A	R	P
M	A	R	C	I	A	N	O		B	R	O	K	A	W		S	S	S
M	Y	F	A	T	H	E	R	S	B	U	S	I	N	E	S	S		
I	N	K	L	E		S	A	O		P	E	T		A	T	E	N	O
			A	S	R		L	U	G			E	S	T	A	T	E	S
B	A	R	B		B	I	B	L	E	K	I	D	S		L	S	A	T
A	P	H	A	S	I	C			M	E	N		T	A	W			
D	O	E	S	A		K	A	A		R	I	C		B	A	S	E	S
		T	H	Y	S	E	R	V	A	N	T	H	E	A	R	E	T	H
M	O	O		H	Y	S	S	O	P		S	O	L	S	T	I	C	E
A	T	R	A	I	N		E	W	O	K		L	I	E				
L	O	I	N		C	A	N	A	L	E	D		O	M	A	S	U	M
L	O	C	K		I	W	I	L	L	S	M	I	T	E	T	H	E	E
E	L	A	L		N	E	D		O	E	I	L		N	E	I	L	L
T	E	L	E		G	T	E		S	Y	N	E		T	E	N	E	T

Answers

Oldies but Goodies (pp. 68–69)

B	A	R	D		H	I	E	R	O		G	O	E	R		A	C	E
A	L	O	E		E	A	T	U	P		R	I	L	E		S	O	P
A	S	O	L	D	A	S	T	H	E	H	I	L	L	S		E	L	I
S	O	F	T	E	R		U	R	N	E	D			I	S	A	A	C
			A	U	T	O			A	W	L		D	N	A			
F	D	R		T	H	O	R	N	I	N	O	N	E	S	S	I	D	E
L	A	U	D		S	H	O	E	R		C	I	A		S	T	A	R
A	D	B	I	Z		S	U	M		B	K	G	D		Y	E	T	I
W	E	E	V	I	L		T	E	T	R		H	S	T		M	A	N
			A	T	O	N	E	S	W	I	T	S	E	N	D			
S	G	T		I	W	O		I	O	T	A		A	P	R	O	N	S
H	O	O	D		D	O	C	S		I	M	A		K	A	R	O	L
O	G	R	E		O	N	O		A	S	P	C	A		B	E	A	U
T	H	E	P	O	W	E	R	S	T	H	A	T	B	E		O	H	M
			T	N	N		R	E	L			S	U	S	A			
B	A	T	H	E			U	M	A	S	S		B	A	R	O	N	S
A	R	E		D	R	O	P	I	N	T	H	E	B	U	C	K	E	T
T	E	N		G	O	A	T		T	B	I	L	L		E	A	V	E
S	A	D		E	N	T	S		A	D	A	M	E		D	Y	E	S

It's a Living (pp. 70–71)

S	A	N	S		S	P	C	A		S	I	T		C	E	D	A	R
W	R	I	T		T	R	I	M		A	R	I		A	L	O	H	A
I	O	T	A		A	I	R	A		T	E	D		M	I	N	E	D
F	A	R	M	E	R	S	C	H	E	E	S	E		E	X	A	M	S
T	R	O	P	I	C	S			L	E	I		S	R	I			
				S	H	I	P	P	I	N	G	C	H	A	R	G	E	S
P	L	U	G		Y	E	L	L		S	N	E	E		S	A	G	A
T	O	N	A	L		R	E	I	T			D	A	S		Y	O	W
A	C	T	N	O	W		A	G	H	A		E	T	T	U			
S	H	O	E	S	O	F	T	H	E	F	I	S	H	E	R	M	A	N
			F	E	E	L		T	O	R	C		E	M	B	O	D	Y
S	H	E		R	I	O			L	I	E	U		S	A	N	D	S
O	U	R	S		S	A	S	K		C	A	N	T		N	O	S	E
Y	E	A	H	I	M	T	H	E	T	A	X	M	A	N				
			A	T	E		A	Y	E			A	L	U	M	N	A	E
C	A	P	R	I		T	H	E	C	A	R	P	E	N	T	E	R	S
L	O	O	P	S		O	D	D		C	A	P	N		G	R	I	T
A	N	N	E	S		F	O	U		I	G	E	T		E	V	O	E
P	E	D	R	O		U	M	P		D	U	D	S		S	E	T	S